EXPERIMENTS IN GENERAL CHEMISTRY

Part I

Second Edition

Barry Rugg

Victoria Russell

New York University

Kendall Hunt
publishing company

Cover photo by Harriet Rugg (deceased).

Kendall Hunt
publishing company

www.kendallhunt.com
Send all inquiries to:
4050 Westmark Drive
Dubuque, IA 52004-1840

CONTENTS

Safety in the Chemistry Laboratory

Prepared by Genya Mallach,
Environmental, Health & Safety Consultant
Emilcott
Chatham, NJ

INTRODUCTION

Your personal safety, and the safety of your colleagues, in a potentially hazardous environment demands that you follow the guidelines described in this chapter. The instructions and guidelines described below provide essential information about the laboratory practices that are considered as the minimum acceptable safe behavior in our laboratories.

All students working in the laboratory are responsible for planning and carrying out each experiment in a manner that will ensure a safe environment to everyone in the facility and with care for university property. Carelessness, or failure to take the following guidelines seriously, is cause for immediate and severe disciplinary action.

Please note, this guide is designed to ensure your safety and others in the chemistry laboratory. Therefore, it is incumbent upon each student to take the proper action to assure that these guidelines are not circumvented.

CONDUCT AND GENERAL HEALTH AND HYGIENE

- Wear appropriate clothing and footwear at all times.
  - No short pants, short skirts, or loose sleeved clothing
  - No exposed midriffs
  - Closed-toe shoes are required at all times (leather preferred).
- Pin up long hair.
- Students can not work alone when handling hazardous materials or performing hazardous procedures.
- Do not deliberately smell or taste a chemical.
- Do not store, heat, eat, or drink food in the laboratory. No gum chewing.
- Never smoke anywhere in the laboratory or building.
- Do not use mouth suction to pipet chemicals or to start a siphon; a pipet bulb or aspirator should be used to provide vacuum.
- Avoid exposure to chemical vapors, fumes, and aerosols. Use appropriate safety equipment whenever such exposure is likely.

- For personal hygiene and safety reasons, wash hands before eating, drinking, or smoking.
- Do not use solvents for washing the skin.
- Never play or horse around.

PERSONAL PROTECTIVE EQUIPMENT

Eye Protection

Thousands of people are blinded each year from work related eye injuries that could have been prevented, if only eye or face protection had been used. Full splash-proof goggles are required **at all times** in the lab.

Emergency eye wash stations are available. The eyewash station discharges a gentle stream of aerated water. A chemical splash into the eyes requires immediate action. Do not wipe or rub the eyes. Go directly to the eyewash fountain, hold the eyelids open with the thumb and forefinger, and let the water flow into the eyes continuously for fifteen minutes until medical help arrives.

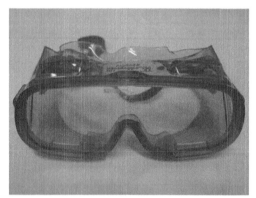

Figure 1.1   Approved   **Figure 1.2**   Not Approved

Chemical Resistant Gloves

Gloves must be worn when working with hazardous chemicals or corrosive liquids. Gloves worn must be made of material known to be resistant to permeation by the chemical of concern. Prior to use, they should be checked for rips, tears and pinholes. Computers and common apparatus are not to be handled while wearing gloves. Gloves contaminated with hazardous chemicals must be disposed of in the **hazardous waste container located in the designated waste bins throughout the lab.**

Lab Coats

Disposable lab coats are required to be worn by students. Lab coats must be worn when working with hazardous chemicals or corrosive liquids.

Respiratory Protection

Good ventilation is essential when working in the chemistry laboratory. *Fume hoods,* or just *hoods,* are laboratory devices that allow us to experiment with volatile or noxious chemicals while isolating their vapors from the laboratory. Hoods have controlled ventilation systems designed to remove chemicals contained in the air before discharge to the environment.

LABORATORY HAZARDS

Chemical Hazards

General

- **DO NOT UNDERESTIMATE THE RISK.** Assume that all chemicals have a risk associated with them and that all substances of unknown toxicity are toxic. Any mixture should be assumed to be more toxic than any of its components.
- **MINIMIZE EXPOSURES TO ANY SUBSTANCE.** Safety precautions will be followed when working with any chemical to avoid eye contact, skin and respiratory exposure.
- **HANDLE HAZARDOUS MATERIALS WITH EXTRA CARE.**
- **NEVER PIPETTE BY MOUTH.**
- **DO NOT DISPOSE OF CHEMICAL BY POURING IT DOWN THE SINK.**
- **LEARN THE PROPERTIES AND HAZARDS OF EACH CHEMICAL BEFORE USING IT.** Each chemical in the laboratory must have a Material Safety Data Sheet (MSDS). At a minimum, the MSDS must include:
  - Identity
  - Manufacturer
  - Ingredients
  - Physical and chemical characteristics
  - Physical hazards
  - Health hazards
  - Proper storage and disposal
- **WHEN NOT IN USE, CHEMICALS SHOULD BE KEPT IN PROPER STORAGE.**

Chemical Storage

Chemicals shall be segregated according to their classes and compatibility and shall be stored in well-ventilated areas with appropriate exhaust systems. Flammable products should be in approved safety containers and stored in areas where the temperature can be modified as needed. Since corrosive chemicals can cause damage to the eyes in an accidental spill, all acids with a pH below 5.0 and all bases with a pH above 9.0 should be stored below eye level as a common practice.

- Limited storage in the laboratory work area is permitted for all EXCEPT extremely toxic and volatile materials (such as carcinogens, reproductive toxins, acute toxic material).
- Proper environmental conditions (temperature, ventilation, and light) must be maintained at all times.
- Fume hoods should not be used for chemical storage.
- Unneeded items should be discarded in an environmentally safe manner or returned to the stockroom.

Figure 1.3

Working with Acids and Bases

- Never store acids and bases together.
- Wear appropriate Personal Protective Equipment (PPE), including goggles, splash shields and chemical resistant gloves when working with these chemicals.
- When preparing an acid solution, always add acid to water, not water to acid.

Working with Solvents

- As a general rule, use solvents in a fume hood. Should their use be required outside the hood, consult your instructor or your professor to assess the necessity of respiratory protection.
- Do not heat flammable solvents over direct flame—a steam bath or heating mantle are safer sources of heat.

Electrical Hazard

The body is primarily water with a good mix of salts, which makes it highly conductive (very low resistance). Ordinary 110-volt house current can be fatal when there is good contact and the victim is grounded.

- All equipment using 110 volts or more must have three-wire grounded connections. Report any equipment not complying with this requirement.
- Authorized maintenance electricians must do all repairs to electrical equipment.
- Do not use equipment that appears to be unsafe, or has exposed or frayed wires. Alert your instructor if you encounter damaged or malfunctioning equipment.

 Water and electricity are a fatal combination!

Blood Borne Pathogens

Blood borne pathogens include human immunodeficiency virus (HIV—the virus that causes AIDS), the hepatitis B virus (HBV), and the hepatitis C virus (HCV). Precautions must be observed in all situations where there is a potential for contact with blood or other potentially infectious materials.

As a universal rule, treat all human blood and certain body fluids as if they are infectious, i.e., do not touch it without protective gloves.

Work surfaces must be decontaminated with an appropriate disinfectant.

- All contaminated work surfaces, tools, objects, etc. should be decontaminated immediately or as soon as feasible after any spill of blood or other potentially infectious materials. A bleach solution or disinfectant must be left in contact with contaminated work surfaces, tools, objects, or potentially infectious materials for at least 10 minutes before cleaning.

- Equipment that may become contaminated with blood or other potentially infectious materials should be examined and decontaminated before servicing or use.

- Broken glassware should not be picked up directly with the hands; sweep or brush material into a dustpan. Alert your instructor if glassware needs to be swept.

LABORATORY EQUIPMENT

Glassware

- The ends of glass tubing and glass rods should always be fire polished.
- When inserting glass tubing, glass rods, and thermometers into a stopper or rubber tubing, use water, oil, grease, or other acceptable lubricant. Wear protective gloves or use a hand towel to protect your hand in the event of a break.
- Pick up large beakers by grasping them around the outside—not by the rim or the lip.
- Do not use chipped/cracked glassware; dispose of it properly.
- Do not pick up any kind of container by the cap.
- Use equipment only for its designated use and avoid damaging laboratory glassware.
- If glassware breaks, alert your instructor to sweep it up right away and place it in a thick-walled carton container.

Figure 1.4

HOUSEKEEPING

→ Take responsiblity for your work area.

→ Designate a "Clean-Up" before leaving the laboratory.

→ Clean up spills or broken glassware immediately.

- Keep the laboratory clean and uncluttered.
- Clean all equipment/tools IMMEDIATELY after use.
- Keep all chemicals properly labeled and stored.
- Students are responsible to clean-up their own work areas.
- Return all equipment and glassware used for that day's experiment.

EMERGENCIES

During the course of normal laboratory operations there is always the potential for an emergency situation to arise. These emergencies can be the result of a chemical spill, fire, or the need for medical assistance.

- If an accident occurs, immediately notify your laboratory instructor.
- In case of a small chemical spill, wash off affected area with cold water for at least 15 minutes.
- If evacuation is required do the following:
  - Leave the building by the designated route.
  - **Walk—Do Not Run.**
  - Do not use elevators.
  - Assemble outside the building at a predetermined location. Your instructor will tell you where to assemble.

 Do not enter the building until an "all clear" message is given.

WASTE DISPOSAL

All used chemicals are to be treated as chemical waste and are to be disposed of as instructed by your lab instructor. Under no circumstances is any chemical waste to be thrown down the drain.

We practice waste minimization in this laboratory. When you obtain reagents, take only as much as you will need for the experiment.

CHEMICAL LABORATORY SAFETY AGREEMENT

When working in the laboratory, I will respect all rules and observe the required lab safety practices outlined in this chapter including the following:

1. Be familiar with the location and operation of all safety equipment.
2. Splash proof goggles are to be worn at all times.
3. Do only assigned experiments and never work alone in the lab.
4. Backpacks, purses, and coats are not permitted in the laboratory and must be in hall lockers.
5. Dispose of waste properly.
   - No waste goes down the drain.
   - Paper waste goes in the large gray bins throughout the lab.
   - Broken glass, rubber gloves, etc. go in the waste bin located between the stockroom doors.
   - Liquid waste goes in the large white drum in the center of the lab unless otherwise specified.
6. Practice waste minimization at all times.
7. Food or drink is not permitted in the lab. Gum is not permitted.
8. Proper dress (for protection) is required at all times.
9. Before leaving the lab, make certain your lab bench is clean and all equipment is in the proper location.
10. Be careful when dispensing chemicals from the fume hoods.
11. Keep analytical equipment such as balances clean and dry at all times.
12. Be careful when working with Bunsen burners, hot plates, and all hot objects.
13. Use good judgment in the laboratory.
14. Read and reread reagent bottles to be certain you are using the correct chemicals.
15. Wash hands before leaving the lab.
16. Report all injuries and accidents immediately to the instructor no matter how minor you think it seems.

I have carefully read the above laboratory safety requirements and understand the importance of compliance with these rules. I will follow these rules when present in the laboratory.

_____

student's signature   date

_____

course title and number   lab section

EXPERIMENT 1: SAFETY LAB EXAM

The Safety Lab Exam is composed of twenty five multiple choice and matching questions, each worth four points.

- You need a score of 80% to pass the lab exam.
- This lab exam is not timed.
- You may take this lab exam multiple times, your highest score will be recorded.
- This lab exam is available until two hours before your scheduled lab period. You must complete and submit the online lab exam before it expires.

2

Measuring Density of Liquids and Solids: Predicting the Salt Content of a Solution from Its Density

BACKGROUND INFORMATION

Properties of a substance are used to identify and distinguish that substance from others. Properties can be either physical or chemical. Chemical properties require chemical change to study while physical properties can be observed by various methods without chemical change. Properties can either be extensive (depending on the quantity of substance) such as mass or volume or intensive (independent of quantity) such as density or index of refraction.

Density, symbolized by ρ (rho), is an important intensive physical property of all substances. Density is the mass per unit volume, $\rho = mass/volume$, usually expressed as g/cm^3 (g/mL), kg/m^3 or lb/ft^3 (English units). Density will vary with temperature because volume changes with temperature. The volume changes for solids and liquids are relatively small while those for gases are much larger.

In this experiment, you will take measurements, do calculations, graph data, and then predict a result from the data you collect. Today, you will measure the density of a solid made of an unknown metal, a rubber stopper, and several liquid solutions. To calculate density, first measure the mass, and then measure the volume. Density will be mass divided by volume. In the chemical laboratory, mass is determined by using either an analytical balance or a top loading balance (see Appendix II).

The density of a solid is measured in two ways depending whether the solid has a regular shape. First measure the mass of the object on an analytical or top loading balance. If the solid has a regular shape—a cube, rectangle, cylinder or sphere, for example—measure the characteristic length, radius, etc. and using the equation for the volume of the object, calculate the volume. Then calculate the density, $\rho = mass/volume$.

If the solid has an irregular shape, measure the volume by displacement of water. First measure the mass of the object. Then measure the volume of the object by displacement. Use an appropriately sized graduated cylinder (the smallest possible will give the most accurate result) and partially fill it with water. Note the initial volume (V_i). Place the object in the graduated cylinder and note the final volume (V_f). The volume of the displaced water is the volume of the object ($V = V_f - V_i$). When reading the volume in a graduated cylinder, the water forms a curved concave surface with the glass called a meniscus. To get consistent results for water or an aqueous solution, measure the volume at the bottom of the meniscus. To do this effectively, your eye should be at the same level as the liquid level. See Appendix III, Fig III.1. Calculate the density of the object, ρ = mass/volume.

To measure the density of a liquid, weigh a graduated cylinder. Partially fill the graduated cylinder with the liquid and weigh again. The mass of the sample is the final less the initial mass of the empty graduated cylinder. Finally, read the volume of liquid in the graduate and calculate the density, ρ = *mass/volume*.

PURPOSE

For density measurements, we will use the analytical balance (or top loading balance when noted) to determine mass and an appropriately sized graduated cylinder to measure volume either directly or by displacement of water. You will measure the density of a rubber stopper and an unknown metal. You will also prepare table salt solutions of various concentrations, and plot the data of density vs. % by mass of the salt in water.

$$\% \text{ by mass} = \frac{\text{mass of salt}}{\text{mass of solution}} \times 100$$

Eq. 2.1

PROCEDURE

Chemical Hazards

• Sodium Chloride may cause skin, eye irritation.

Care should be taken when working with this reagent. Avoid inhalation and contact with skin, eyes, and clothing. Goggles, gloves, and lab coats are required at all times.

Part I—Density of Salt Solutions

A. Preparation of Salt Solutions:

1. Obtain three clean, dry 250 mL beakers and label them 1, 2 & 3.
2. Obtain a wash bottle and fill it with deionized water.
3. Using a top loading balance, weigh approximately 100 g of deionized water in each beaker and record the exact mass of the water on Data Sheet I.
4. Beaker 1 will remain pure deionized water. Pre-weigh between 5–6 g of common salt (NaCl) and add it to Beaker 2. Weigh the exact mass of beaker with water and salt and record it on Data Sheet I. Calculate the actual mass of salt added.
5. Pre-weigh 11–12 g of salt and add it to Beaker 3. Again, record the exact mass of beaker with water and salt, and calculate the actual mass of salt added.
6. Using a glass stirring rod, mix the solutions in Beakers 2 and 3 until the salt is dissolved. Calculate the mass % of salt solution in each solution and record your result in Data Sheet I. KEEP THE SOLUTIONS FOR PART B!

B. Measure the Density of the Salt Solutions and of Pure Water:

1. For the remainder of the experiment, you will use an analytical balance. Mass a clean, dry 10 mL graduated cylinder.

2. Add between 9 and 10 mL of pure water from Beaker 1.

3. Mass the graduated cylinder with pure water.

4. Measure the exact volume of the pure water using the graduated cylinder.

5. Repeat steps 1−4 a second time for the pure water in Beaker 1.

6. Repeat steps 1−4 as necessary to perform two trials each for the solutions in Beakers 2 and 3.

7. Calculate the density for each of the two solutions and the pure water. Be certain to show a sample calculation each time a number is calculated and use the correct number of significant figures (see Appendix IV). Your final result will be the calculated mean.

8. Use the Logger Pro© software to plot the data, mean density (g/mL) on the y-axis vs. % by mass salt in water on the x-axis. There are three points to be plotted. 0.0% salt, and your exact values that are approximately 5% and 10% salt.

9. Use the linear function to draw a best fit straight line through the three points. Under "Graph Options" uncheck "connect points" and check the "point protector" box,

10. Title the graph *"Density vs. % Salt (NaCl) by Mass in Water."* Both partners should have their names on the graph. **Print** this graph.

11. When you have completed this experiment, be sure to log out of your computer before shutting it down.

Part II—Density of a Rubber Stopper

1. Obtain a rubber stopper.

2. Using a 50 mL graduated cylinder, determine the density by the method described in the background section for an irregularly shaped object.

3. Conduct three independent trials and record your results in Data Sheet II. Show a sample calculation each time a number is calculated and use the correct number of significant figures (see Appendix IV). Calculate the mean and standard deviation (Appendix IB).

Part III—Density of an Unknown Metal

1. Obtain one of the three unknown metal samples.

2. Using a 10mL graduated cylinder, determine the density of the metal by the method described in the background section for an irregularly shaped object.

3. Conduct three independent trials and record your results in Data Sheet III. Show a sample calculation each time a number is calculated and use the correct number of significant figures (see Appendix IV). Using the density, identify the unknown metal from the list below.

Metal	Density (g/cm^3)
Stainless steel	8.03
Magnesium	1.74
Copper	8.92
Silver	10.5
Aluminum	2.70
Brass	8.50

DATA SHEET I

PART I

- Show a sample calculation for each type of calculated value.

A. Prepare Salt Solutions

	Beaker 1	Beaker 2	Beaker 3
Mass of beaker	_____	_____	_____
Mass of beaker + water	_____	_____	_____
Mass of water	_____	_____	_____
Mass of beaker + water + salt	_____	_____	_____
Mass of salt	_____	_____	_____
Mass of salt + water	_____	_____	_____
Mass % salt	_____	_____	_____

B. Measure Density of Salt Solutions

	Beaker 1		Beaker 2		Beaker 3	
Trial #	1	2	1	2	1	2
Mass of graduated cylinder						
Mass of cylinder + solution						
Mass of solution						
Volume of solution						
Density of solution						
Mean density	_____		_____		_____	

15

DATA SHEET II

PART II

- Show a sample calculation for each type of calculated value.

A. Density of a Rubber Stopper

Trial #	1	2	3
Mass of rubber stopper	_____	_____	_____
Initial volume of water	_____	_____	_____
Final volume with stopper	_____	_____	_____
Volume of stopper	_____	_____	_____
Density of stopper	_____	_____	_____
Mean value	_____		
Standard deviation	_____		

DATA SHEET III

PART III

- Show a sample calculation for each type of calculated value.

A. Density of an Unknown Metal

Unknown Metal Code: _____

Trial #	1	2	3
Mass of metal	_____	_____	_____
Initial volume of water	_____	_____	_____
Final volume with metal	_____	_____	_____
Volume of metal	_____	_____	_____
Density of metal	_____	_____	_____
Mean value	_____		
Standard deviation	_____		

B. Identity of the Metal

Post-Laboratory Questions

1. A beaker contains a clear colorless liquid and you forgot to label it. How can you be sure if it's pure water or if it contains dissolved common salt? (Do not taste it.)

2. Archimedes' Principle states that when an object is immersed in a fluid, the buoyant force is equal to the weight of the fluid displaced by the object. The weight of an object is equal to its mass times the acceleration due to gravity and to the weight of the fluid displaced by the object. The buoyant force opposes the weight of the immersed object. The weight of the fluid displaced is equal to the volume of the fluid displaced times the density of the fluid times the acceleration due to gravity.

   Weight (N, newtons) = mass (kg) $\times$ g. At sea level, g = 9.81 m/s^2.

   A cube of lead ($\rho = 11.3 \times 10^3$ kg/m^3) is placed in a pool of mercury ($\rho = 13.6 \times 10^3$ kg/m^3). The cube of lead is 3.60×10^2 cm on a side. Calculate the percentage of the cube that is above the pool of mercury.

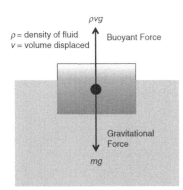

ρ = density of fluid
v = volume displaced

$\rho v g$

Buoyant Force

Gravitational Force

mg

3. Carbon monoxide is a toxic pollutant found in our city air. On a particular day, the air contains 6.50 mg of CO per 1.000×10^3 cubic meter of air. How many grams of CO are present in a room whose dimensions are 15.0 meters $\times$ 11.0 meters $\times$ 16.5 meters?

4. The bromine content of average ocean water is 65 parts per million. Assuming 100 percent recovery, how many cubic meters of ocean water must be processed to produce 0.75 kg of bromine? Assume the density of seawater is 1.023×10^3 kg/m^3.

BEFORE YOU COME TO LAB YOU MUST COMPLETE A PRELAB ASSIGNMENT:

Experiment 2: Measuring Density of Liquids and Solids Online PRELAB Quiz:

- The online Measuring Density of Liquids and Solids PRELAB Quiz is composed of multiple choice questions.

- The PRELAB score accounts for 40 points of your total lab score.

- The PRELAB quiz is timed, and it must be submitted before **11:59 pm the night before your experiment.**

- You may only submit the PRELAB quiz once.

- In order to prepare for your PRELAB quiz, it is recommended that you study the background information, calculations, and lab procedure for the experiment in your lab manual. You may be asked to perform calculations; the correct answer will need to be reported to the proper number of significant figures and with the appropriate units.

- You may be asked to prepare and print out a graph that you will turn into your instructors when you come to lab.

3

Separation and Identification of Food Dyes by Paper Chromatography

BACKGROUND INFORMATION

Chromatography

Chromatography is an analytical separation technique that takes advantage of the differences in attraction or affinity between a solvent phase and the components of a mixture. Since no chemical changes occur to the components during separation, chromatography is considered a physical rather than a chemical separation.

To separate components using chromatography, a mixture is dissolved into a gas or liquid called the **mobile phase**. The mobile phase then moves over a solid (or viscous liquid) component called the **stationary phase**. The components of the mixture will separate based on their relative affinities for either the mobile or stationary phase. A component with a greater affinity for the mobile phase will move farther and faster along the stationary phase than a component with greater affinity for the stationary phase. A component more attracted to the stationary phase than the mobile phase will move more slowly, or over a shorter distance.

Affinity for either phase is based on the structure and electrostatic forces of the components. A more **polar** molecule (a molecule with an unequal distribution of electric charge) will be attracted preferentially to the more polar phase.

Types of Chromatography

Chemical and biological laboratories employ several types of chromatography to separate mixtures.

Gas-liquid Chromatography: The mobile phase is an inert gas, which carries vaporized components through a tube containing the stationary phase. The components emerge from the tube separated. This technique is useful for separating mixtures of gases or components that can be vaporized without thermally decomposing, such as hydrocarbon mixtures.

High-performance Liquid Chromatography (HPLC): Components that would decompose if they were vaporized, such as proteins, complex carbohydrates, and other biological molecules can be separated via liquid chromatography. As the name suggests, the mobile phase is a liquid. The mobile phase is forced through the solid stationary phase under high pressure.

Both gas and liquid chromatography use a detector as components emerge from the stationary phase to identify and determine relative amounts of the constituents.

Thin Layer Chromatography (TLC): Here, a thin layer of silica gel, alumina, or cellulose on a glass plate serves as the stationary phase. Solvent is drawn through the stationary phase using capillary action. TLC is similar to paper chromatography, but has the advantage of faster runs and better separations of components.

Paper Chromatography

We will be separating and identifying components of food dyes using **paper chromatography**. The sample to be separated is placed on chromatography paper—the stationary phase. The paper is then placed in a **solvent** which acts as the mobile phase. The solvent is drawn up the paper through **capillary action**; the solvent moves up the paper because the solvent is attracted to water molecules that are permanently bound to the cellulose fibers in the paper.

To perform separation through paper chromatography, the mixture is spotted a fixed distance from the bottom edge on the **origin line**. The chromatography paper is then placed in a beaker with the solvent, and the solvent is drawn up the paper. When the leading edge of the solvent (the **solvent front**) reaches the mixture the components (analytes) will begin to separate based on their relative affinities for either the stationary or mobile phase.

The paper must be removed from the solvent **before** the solvent front reaches the top of the paper. This will allow us to measure the distance the solvent moves from the origin line.

Knowing the distances that the individual components and the solvent front move allows us to quantify the separation by determining the **Retention Factor** of each component.

$$R_f = \frac{\text{distance the analyte has traveled}}{\text{distance the solvent has traveled}}$$ Eq. 3.1

The retention factor is a unitless ratio that determines the relative affinities of components for the solvent. Retention factors range between 0.0 and 1.0. An R_f close to zero indicates the component has a strong attraction for the stationary phase, while an R_f close to one indicates a relatively strong attraction for the mobile phase.

The R_f value for a particular component-solvent system is reproducible under controlled experimental conditions. A solvent system that gives the greatest difference in retention factors gives the greatest separation, or **resolution**.

Figure 3.1 compares two chromatograms. The chromatogram on the left has achieved good resolution for all components, while the one on the right has not.

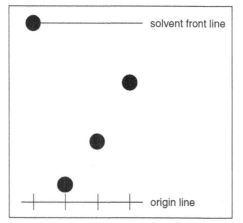 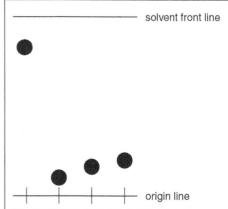

Figure 3.1   Chromatogram where good resolution is achieved (Left)
Chromatogram where components of mixture are NOT resolved (Right)

Dyes for Foods, Drugs, and Cosmetics (FD&C)

Federal legislation to regulate food dyes dates back to 1906 when Congress passed the Pure Food and Drug Act. The Act created the Food & Drug Administration (FDA) to oversee additives in food products. In 1938 the Federal Food, Drug and Cosmetic Act further restricted the use of dyes and gave the FDA control of dyes allowed in food, drug or cosmetic applications.

Subsequent research has found that some of the dyes approved for use in 1938 were toxic or carcinogenic. Red 2 and red 4 were removed from the list of legal food colorings in the United States in 1976, although red 2 is still used in other countries as a food additive.

The Food and Drug Administration (FDA) currently lists seven certified food, drug, and cosmetic dyes (FD&C) as approved additives in food products: red 3, red 40, yellow 5, yellow 6, green 3, blue 1, and blue 2.

Figure 3.2 depicts the chemical structures of the seven approved dyes. Note that all are structurally similar. All seven have conjugated systems, long carbon structures with alternating single and double bonds between the carbons. Often such extensively conjugated molecules are brightly colored. All seven dyes are also sodium salts of sulfonic acids (or carboxylic acid in the case of red 3); this makes the dyes water soluble.

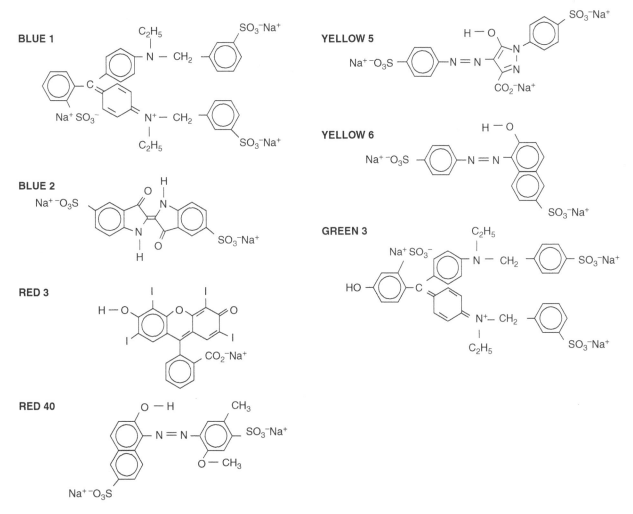

Figure 3.2 Structures of the seven certified food dyes

Preparation of a Mixture of Food Dyes; Chromatography

You will be developing chromatograms of the FDA-approved food dyes and two unknowns in four different solvent systems. You will choose the two best solvent systems and then use the R_f values and colors of the food dyes to identify the unknowns.

PURPOSE

1. Investigate solvent systems for separation of dyes in paper chromatography.
2. Separate and identify the components of a mixture of dyes using paper chromatography.

PROCEDURE

> **Chemical Hazards**
>
> • Ethanol (95%): flammable liquid and vapor. Irritating to eyes and skin. May cause respiratory irritation. Some ethanols contain trace amounts of benzene or methanol, both of which are very toxic.
>
> Care should be taken when working with this reagent. Avoid inhalation and contact with skin, eyes, and clothing. If accidentally ingested, consult poison control immediately. Goggles, gloves, and lab coats are required at all times.

Comparing Solvents for Elution of FD&C Dyes in Paper Chromatography

1. Ask your instructor to assign you two unknown dye mixtures.
2. Prepare four chromatography papers in the following fashion:
   a. Obtain an 8 cm × 15 cm piece of chromatography paper.
   b. Using a pencil, not a pen, draw a line across the long axis of the paper 1 cm from the bottom. (See Figure 3.3)
   c. Beginning 1.5 cm from the left edge, make small pencil marks every 1 cm on the origin line.
   d. Label these marks: B1, B2, Y5, Y6, R3, R40, and G3.
   e. Continue marking for the mixtures: B1 and R40, B1 and Y5, R3 and Y6, and B2 and Y5.
   f. Label two marks for your two assigned unknown dye mixtures.
   g. Make a small mark 2 cm from the top of the chromatography paper. When the solvent front reaches this mark you will remove the chromatogram from the solvent.
3. Label the top of each chromatogram from A to D.
4. On a glass plate, carefully place a small drop of each of the dyes onto labeled portions on the glass. Be careful not to contaminate the droppers with other dyes.
5. Create the mixtures (part 2e above) by mixing a small drop of each of the individual dyes on the glass using a wooden toothpick.
6. Using a clean wooden toothpick, spot a **very** small amount of each dye onto the chromatography papers on its respective mark on the origin lines. You should practice with each dye on a spare piece of chromatography paper before attempting

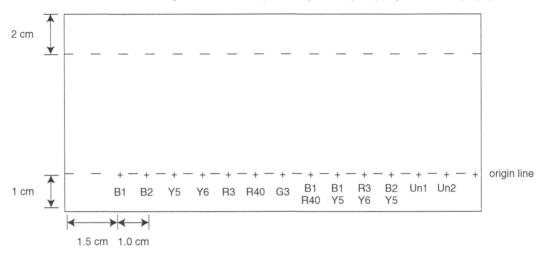

Figure 3.3 Marking chromatography paper

to spot your actual chromatogram. The spots should be about 1 mm in diameter. Check your dye spotting with your instructors before running your chromatogram.

7. Carefully roll up each piece of chromatography paper along the short side with the dye spots facing out. Staple the ends of the paper together. The ends should touch but NOT overlap.

8. In a clean 50 mL beaker, obtain approximately 10 mL of 0.1% salt solution. In a second 50 mL beaker, obtain approximately 15 mL of 95% ethanol. Finally, in a third 50 mL beaker obtain approximately 30 mL of deionized water.

9. Label a 600 mL beaker as WASTE.

10. Prepare four 250 mL beakers with the following solvents:
    a. 7 mL of 0.1% salt solution
    b. 7 mL of deionized water
    c. 4 mL of deionized water + 4 mL of 95% ethanol
    d. 2 mL of deionized water + 6 mL of 95% ethanol

11. Carefully place each of the labeled chromatography papers into their corresponding beaker (A–D). Cover each beaker with a Petri dish cover. This will prevent the evaporation of a volatile solvent and ensure that the air in the container remains saturated with solvent vapor. Make sure the paper cylinders do not touch the walls of the beakers. Note the time the cylinders are inserted on Data Sheet I.

12. Remove the cylinders from the beakers when the solvent levels are approximately 2.0 cm from the top of the paper. Not all four will finish at the same time. On Data Sheet I, note the time the solvent front of each chromatogram reaches 2 cm from the top of the paper.

13. Carefully remove the staples and mark the final solvent line (in pencil) on the chromatograms. The solvent front must be marked after it stops moving, but before the solvent has completely dried. Wait until the paper is partially dry to minimize the risk of tearing.

14. Characterize the chromatograms (with respect to the food dyes) following the directions given on the next page.

15. Compare the R_f values for each of the four chromatograms and select the two solvent systems that lead to the best resolution.

16. Characterize the two selected chromatograms with respect to the unknowns. Each unknown food dye mixture contains anywhere from two to five different components.

Characterize the chromatograms using Data Sheets I through III. Summarize your results and identify the dyes present in each unknown mixture on Data Sheet IV. Your chromatograms will be handed in to your Instructors with your lab report. Write both partner's names and your lab bench # on the back of each chromatogram. Staple the chromatograms to your lab report.

Analyzing and Characterizing Chromatograms

1. Measure the distance the solvent moved (from the origin to the solvent line).

2. Using a pencil, draw around the perimeter of each of the dye spots in the chromatogram. Mark the center of each spot.

3. Measure the distance from the origin to the center of each spot.

4. Calculate the R_f for each of the dyes.

DATA SHEET I

EVALUATING SOLVENT SYSTEMS

- Show a sample calculation for each type of calculated value.

Chromatogram	Distance Solvent Moved	Time Start	Time End	Time Elapsed
A	_____	_____	_____	_____
B	_____	_____	_____	_____
C	_____	_____	_____	_____
D	_____	_____	_____	_____

Dye	A		B		C		D	
	Dist	R_f	Dist	R_f	Dist	R_f	Dist	R_f
B1								
B2								
Y5								
Y6								
R3								
R40								
G3								
Mix1								
B1								
R40								
Mix2								
B1								
Y5								
Mix3								
R3								
Y6								
Mix4								
B2								
Y5								

DATA SHEET II

ANALYZING UNKNOWNS

- Show a sample calculation for each type of calculated value.

Code numbers of Unknowns: _____   _____

Solvent System 1: _____

Distance Solvent Front Moved: _____

	Unknown 1	*Unknown 2*
Component		
Color	_____	_____
Distance	_____	_____
R_f	_____	_____
Component		
Color	_____	_____
Distance	_____	_____
R_f	_____	_____
Component		
Color	_____	_____
Distance	_____	_____
R_f	_____	_____
Component		
Color	_____	_____
Distance	_____	_____
R_f	_____	_____
Component		
Color	_____	_____
Distance	_____	_____
R_f	_____	_____

DATA SHEET III

- Show a sample calculation for each type of calculated value.

Solvent System 2: _____   Distance Solvent Front Moved: _____

	Unknown 1	*Unknown 2*
Component		
Color	_____	_____
Distance	_____	_____
R_f	_____	_____
Component		
Color	_____	_____
Distance	_____	_____
R_f	_____	_____
Component		
Color	_____	_____
Distance	_____	_____
R_f	_____	_____
Component		
Color	_____	_____
Distance	_____	_____
R_f	_____	_____
Component		
Color	_____	_____
Distance	_____	_____
R_f	_____	_____

DATA SHEET IV

- Show a sample calculation for each type of calculated value.

IDENTIFYING THE COMPONENTS

Unknown 1: code number _____

Component Color	_____	_____	_____	_____	_____
R_f (Solvent 1)	_____	_____	_____	_____	_____
R_f (Solvent 2)	_____	_____	_____	_____	_____
Identity	_____	_____	_____	_____	_____

Unknown 2: code number _____

Component Color	_____	_____	_____	_____	_____
R_f (Solvent 1)	_____	_____	_____	_____	_____
R_f (Solvent 2)	_____	_____	_____	_____	_____
Identity	_____	_____	_____	_____	_____

Post-Laboratory Questions

1. For the two unknown dye mixtures, describe the component dyes in each. What process did you use to arrive at these conclusions?

   b. Briefly explain your choice of solvent systems for the identification of the unknowns. What factor(s) affected your decision? Explain.

2. Let us investigate another chromatography technique known as two-dimensional chromatography. This technique is very powerful for separating mixtures of dyes. One spot containing a mixture of components is spotted on the origin line at the right-most corner of the chromatography paper. The chromatogram is run in a solvent. After it is dried, the chromatography paper is turned 90° to the right, remade into a cylinder, and run a second time without re-spotting. This will give you a 2D chromatogram for your dye mixture.

    a. First, draw the chromatogram you would expect from spotting a mixture of G3, B1, R3, and Y5 on the right hand corner and running the chromatogram in a 0.1% salt solution.

    b. Draw a second picture showing the 2D chromatogram you would expect after taking the chromatogram from part a, rotating it 90° to the right and running it in a second solvent system, the 75% ethanol in water mixture.

3. Explain how the chromatographic results will be affected if you do the following:
   a. Mark the chromatography paper using a pen
   b. The spots are too large
   c. The solvent level in the developing beaker was above the baseline
   d. Forget to close the developing beaker with a watch glass

BEFORE YOU COME TO LAB YOU MUST COMPLETE A PRELAB ASSIGNMENT:

Experiment 3: Separation and Identification of Food Dyes by Paper Chromatography Online PRELAB Quiz:

- The Separation and Identification of Food Dyes by Paper Chromatography Online PRELAB Quiz is composed of multiple choice questions.
- The PRELAB score accounts for 40 points of your total lab score.
- The PRELAB quiz is timed, and it must be submitted before **11:59 pm the night before your experiment.**
- You may only submit the PRELAB quiz once.
- In order to prepare for your PRELAB quiz, it is recommended that you study the background information, calculations, and lab procedure for the experiment in your lab manual. You may be asked to perform calculations; the correct answer will need to be reported to the proper number of significant figures and with the appropriate units.
- You may be asked to prepare and print out a graph that you will turn into your instructors when you come to lab.
- Some Questions on the Prelab Quiz refers to Figure 3.4 Below. NOTE: A metric ruler is required to complete the Prelab assignment.

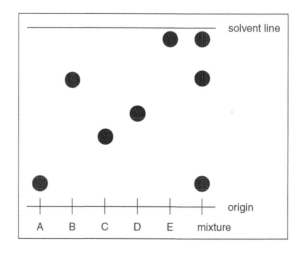

Figure 3.4

Naming Inorganic Chemicals

BACKGROUND INFORMATION

A set of rules called the **Stock System** is used to categorize and ultimately name inorganic chemical compounds.

Oxidation is a process that takes place in the formation of many chemical compounds. Oxidation is the loss of electrons leaving the subject atom electron deficient with a positive charge. These positively charged atoms are usually **metal ions** and are called **cations.** Whenever oxidation takes place, reduction or the addition of electrons must also take place. The species which accept the electrons are usually **non-metals** and are called **anions.** Oxidation and reduction take place simultaneously and are called **redox** reactions. When oxidation takes place, the species that is oxidized is called the reducing agent while the species being reduced is called the oxidizing agent. Electrons transferred in this way must be balanced in the same way that atoms on each side of a chemical equation must be balanced.

Compounds can be either ionic or covalent in character. Ionic compounds usually consist of a metal and a non-metal and one or more electrons are transferred from the metal to the non-metal. The positively charged cation is attracted to the negatively charged anion forming an ionic bond. Covalent compounds are compounds where electrons are shared. These compounds usually consist of two non-metals.

The property that determines the character of the bond formed, whether ionic, covalent, or something in between, is the electronegativity of the element or its tendency to attract an electron. Elements with large differences in electronegativity tend to form ionic compounds while those with electronegativities of similar magnitude form covalent compounds.

In naming inorganic compounds, an important factor to determine is the **oxidation state** of each atom in the compound. Where electrons have been transferred, the oxidation state equals the charge on the ion. **Oxidation numbers** are assigned in the cases where electrons may not have been transferred.

Assigning Oxidation Numbers

a. In free elements, each atom has an oxidation number of zero.

b. For monatomic ions, the oxidation number is equal to the charge on the ion.

c. The oxidation number of oxygen in most compounds is -2 (except in peroxides it is -1).

  d. The oxidation number of hydrogen is $+1$ in most compounds (it is -1 when hydrogen is bonded to a metal or boron in a binary compound).

  e. Fluorine has an oxidation number of -1 in *all* of its compounds. Other halogens (Cl, Br, and I) have negative oxidation numbers when they occur as halide ions in their compounds. They can have positive oxidation numbers when combined with oxygen or another halogen.

  f. In a neutral molecule, the sum of the oxidation numbers of all the atoms must be zero. In a polyatomic ion, the sum of the oxidation numbers of all atoms must equal the net charge of the ion.

Given a chemical formula, first we must categorize the compound and if necessary, determine the oxidation state of each element. Use the flow chart below to categorize the compounds.

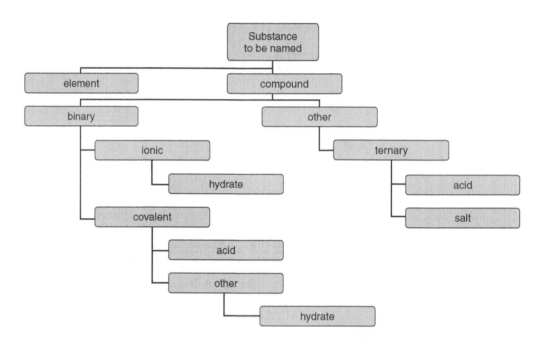

Naming Binary Compounds

Ionic Binary Compounds

Ionic binary compounds are salts, usually a metal + non-metal, named for the ions.

For example: $MgCl_2$

Name of Cation	Name of Anion
magnesium	chloride

Cation names are metals named for element. Sometimes metals have more than one form or multiple oxidation states, then we use Roman numerals in parenthesis.

For example:
- Cu(I)   and   Cu(II)—copper 1 and 2
- Fe(II)   and   Fe(III)—iron 2 and 3

We use only one non-metal cation, NH_4^+, the ammonium ion which is *polyatomic.*

An anion name where the anion is a single element (monatomic), is simply the name of the element where the ending of the name is replaced by **ide.** So that chlorine becomes chlor**ide,** oxygen becomes ox**ide** and nitrogen becomes nitr**ide.**

For example:

- ZnI_2 zinc iodide
- CuO copper(II) oxide
- Cr_2O_3 chromium(III) oxide

Covalent Binary Compounds

Covalent compounds are those in which electrons are shared and are usually composed of only nonmetals. Naming is similar to ionic compounds only we use prefixes to show number of atoms present in molecules

prefix	meaning
mono-	1
di-	2
tri-	3
tetra-	4
penta-	5
hexa-	6
hepta-	7
octa-	8
nona-	9
deca-	10

For example:

- CO carbon monoxide
- PCl_3 phosphorus trichloride
- CCl_4 carbon tetrachloride

Molecular compounds with "common names"

- H_2O water
- PH_3 phosphine
- CH_4 methane
- NH_3 ammonia
- SiH_4 silane
- B_2H_6 diborane

Naming Binary Acids—Covalent Compounds

The name of a binary acid is related to the name of the anion. Anions with names that end in "ide" have associated acids with the "hydro-" prefix and an "-ic" suffix. In "pure" form, HCl is hydrogen chloride gas and should be written HCl(g). If we add water, H^+ cations form along with the monatomic anion Cl^-. We write HCl(aq), named hydrochloric acid.

Examples:

- HF(aq)   hydrofluoric acid
- H_2S(aq)   hydrosulfuric acid

Ternary Compounds

Ternary ionic compounds consist of three elements and usually contain oxygen within the polyatomic anion. The polyatomic anions are covalently bonded; however, the anions form ionic compounds with metals in the same way as binary ionics are formed. The names of these polyatomic anions require memorization. A representative list is given below and more extensive lists can be found in your text and many other sources.

- Example: Na_2SO_4

	Name cation		Name anion
	sodium		sulfate

Representative Polyatomic Anions

OH^-	hydroxide	CO_3^{2-}	carbonate	PO_4^{3-}	phosphate
CN^-	cyanide	SO_3^{2-}	sulfite	PO_3^{3-}	phosphite
HCO_3^-	bicarbonate	SO_4^{2-}	sulfate	BO_3^{3-}	borate
	hydrogen carbonate	HPO_4^{2-}	hydrogen phosphate		
NO_2^-	nitrite	CrO_4^{2-}	chromate		
NO_3^-	nitrate	$C_2O_4^{2-}$	oxalate		
$CH_3CO_2^-$	acetate	O_2^{2-}	peroxide		
$H_2PO_4^-$	dihydrogen phosphate	$Cr_2O_7^{2-}$	dichromate		
HSO_4^-	hydrogen sulfate				
ClO^-	hypochlorite				
ClO_2^-	chlorite				
ClO_3^-	chlorate				
ClO_4^-	perchlorate				
MnO_4^-	permanganate				
SCN^-	thiocyanate				

Ternary Acids

The name depends on the polyatomic anion. Oxoacids are acids, even when "pure," and thus the "(aq)" is not required.

Oxoanion		Oxoacid	
Perchlor**ate** ion	ClO_4^-	**Per**chlor**ic** acid	$HClO_4$
Chlor**ate** ion	ClO_3^-	Chlor**ic** acid	$HClO_3$
Chlor**ite** ion	ClO_2^-	Chlor**ous** acid	$HClO_2$
Hypochlor**ite** ion	ClO^-	**Hypo**chlor**ous** acid	$HClO$

Oxidation state of chlorine changes through series from $+7$ to $+1$. The most common ion gets the ate ending.

For sulfur, the most common is SO_4^{2-} (sulfate) which corresponds to sulfuric acid.

Oxoanion		Oxoacid	
Sulf**ate** ion	SO_4^{2-}	Sulfur**ic** acid	H_2SO_4
Sulf**ite** ion	SO_3^{2-}	Sulfur**ous** acid	H_2SO_3
Hyposulf**ite** ion	SO_2^{2-}	**Hypo**sulfur**ous** acid	H_2SO_2

Naming Hydrates

Hydrates are compounds that have a specific number of water molecules attached. They are generally formed from aqueous solution. The water molecules are trapped in crystal and can be driven off by heating.

Examples of hydrates:

- $CuSO_4 \cdot 5H_2O$ copper(II) sulfate pentahydrate
- $LiCl \cdot H_2O$ lithium chloride monohydrate

EXPERIMENT 4: NAMING INORGANIC COMPOUNDS ONLINE EXAM

PLEASE READ INSTRUCTIONS CAREFULLY BEFORE BEGINNING EXAM

- The Naming Inorganic Compounds Online Exam is composed of fifty multiple choice and fill-in-the blank questions.
- This lab exam is not timed.
- You may submit the completed lab exam only once.
- This lab exam is **available until two hours before your scheduled lab period**. See the syllabus for due date.
- You must complete and submit the online lab exam before it expires.
- In multiple choice format you will be asked to choose the appropriate chemical formula given the name.
- You will be asked two forms of fill in the blank questions: to assign oxidation charges or to provide the name given a chemical formula.
- When asked to provide the oxidation number provide the sign of the charge and the numeral

Some examples:
- CORRECT: -1
- INCORRECT: minus one
- CORRECT: $+1$
- INCORRECT: plus one
- You will not receive credit for misspelled names.
- When asked to provide the chemical name DO NOT capitalize the the first letters of a name.
- Roman numerals SHOULD be capitalized and in parentheses. There should NOT be a space between the parentheses and the metal cation name.

Some examples:
- CORRECT: lead(II) oxide
- INCORRECT: Lead (II) oxide
- CORRECT: hypochlorous acid
- INCORRECT: Hypochlorous acid

Print Name: _____ Date: _____ Lab Bench #: _____

PRACTICE (Only the online portion
of the Experiment will be graded)

1. Name these ionic binary compounds:

   a. $CaBr_2$ _____

   b. FeO _____

   c. Fe_2O_3 _____

   d. $SrCl_2$ _____

   e. MnI_3 _____

2. Assign oxidation numbers to the metal ions in these ionic compounds:

   a. Hg_2Br_2 _____

   b. FeO _____

   c. Fe_2O_3 _____

   d. SrI_2 _____

   e. Li_3N _____

3. Name these covalent binary compounds:

   a. $HI(aq)$ _____

   b. PBr_5 _____

   c. HCl _____

   d. N_2O_5 _____

   e. SCl_2 _____

4. Write the chemical formulas for these binary covalent compounds:

    a. dinitrogen tetroxide   _____

    b. disulfur decafluoride   _____

    c. carbon disulfide   _____

    d. silicon carbide   _____

    e. hydrogen sulfide   _____

5. Name these ternary salts:

    a. $Al_2(SO_4)_3$ _____

    b. $Ni(ClO_3)_2$ _____

    c. $Ca(H_2PO_4)_2$ _____

    d. Hg_2SO_3 _____

    e. $Cu_2Cr_2O_7$ _____

6. Name these ternary acids:

    a. HIO_4 _____

    b. HIO _____

    c. $HClO_3$ _____

    d. $HCN(aq)$ _____

    e. H_2SO_4 _____

7. Write the chemical formulas for these ternary acids:

    a. phosphorous acid   _____

    b. chloric acid   _____

    c. bromic acid   _____

    d. acetic acid   _____

    e. perbromic acid   _____

8. Write the chemical formulas for these ternary salts:

    a. lithium aluminum hydride   _____

    b. lead(IV) acetate   _____

    c. magnesium hydroxide   _____

    d. lithium carbonate   _____

    e. cesium hydroxide   _____

9. Name these hydrates:

    a. $CaCl_2 \cdot 2H_2O$ _____

    b. $Ba(NO_3)_2 \cdot 4H_2O$ _____

10. Write the chemical formulas for these ternary salts:

    a. iron(II) nitrate hexahydrate   _____

    b. manganese(II) acetate   _____
        hexahydrate

11. Name the following:

    a. O_2 _____

    b. $NaHSO_4$ _____

    c. $LiClO_4 \cdot 3H_2O$ _____

12. Write the chemical formulas for these:

    a. bromous acid   _____

    b. aluminum fluoride   _____

    c. cobalt(II) bromate   _____

5

Introduction to the LabQuest© Interface

PURPOSE

The purpose of this experiment is to become familiar with the computer, the LabQuest©
computer interface, and some of its associated probes and the Logger Pro© software to
learn the basics of data analysis. You will conduct volume measurements and a titration
according to the methods of Appendix III.

In today's experiment, you will measure:

1. Temperature vs. time (graph 1)
2. Temperature change of water after mixing with a given volume of hot water (graph 2)
3. The temperature and pH change when mixing acid and base (graphs 3 & 4)
4. Titration using the pH meter (graph 5 and 6)
5. Simple curve fitting and interpolation in data analysis (graphs 7 & 8)

Today you will be measuring the temperature and pH of your solutions.

The pH of a solution is the quantitative measure of acidity and is related to the
hydronium ion, or H^+ ion, also written as H_3O^+ concentration in solution. The brackets
shown, $[H^+]$, means "molarity of H^+" and molarity means moles per liter of solution.

$$pH = -\log[H^+] \qquad\qquad \text{Eq. 5.1}$$

$$[H^+] = 10^{-pH} \text{ (antilog)} \qquad\qquad \text{Eq. 5.2}$$

Become familiar with the "log" function on your calculator.

We have to be able to compute pH from hydrogen ion concentration and then from
pH, convert to hydrogen ion concentration. The significant figure rules for logariths are
different from what we've seen before as illustrated below:

The hydrogen ion concentration in pure water at 25°C is $1.0 \times 10^{-7} M$

$$[H^+] = 1.0 \times 10^{-7} \text{ moles/liter} \qquad \text{2 significant figures}$$

Applying the definition of pH, the pH of pure water equals 7.00.

$$pH = -\log (1.0 \times 10^{-7}) = 7.00 \qquad \text{2 significant figures}$$

Significant figures when expressing logarithms such as pH count only the digits to the right of the decimal point. The digit(s) to the left of the decimal is (are) related to the exponent. This topic is considered more thoroughly in Appendix I.E.

We will use the LabQuest$^©$ pH probe to monitor pH.

In any aqueous solution:

$$[H^+][OH^-] = 1.0 \times 10^{-14} \text{ @ } 25°C \qquad \text{Eq. 5.3}$$

Therefore, given one of either $[H^+]$, $[OH^-]$, or pH, we can calculate the other two values.

Sample Calculation 1: The $[H_3O^+]$ concentration in an aqueous solution is 3.6×10^{-6}. Calculate the solution pH and the $[OH^-]$.

$$pH = -\log[3.6 \times 10^{-6}] = 5.44$$

$$[OH^-] = \frac{1.0 \times 10^{-14}}{3.6 \times 10^{-6} \, M} = 2.8 \times 10^{-9} M$$

Sample Calculation 2: The pH of a solution is 2.85. Calculate the $[H_3O^+]$ and the $[OH^-]$.

$$pH = 2.85$$

$$[H_3O^+] = 10^{-pH} = 10^{-2.85} = 1.4 \times 10^{-3} M$$

$$[OH^-] = \frac{1.0 \times 10^{-14}}{1.4 \times 10^{-3} M} = 7.1 \times 10^{-12} M$$

INSTRUMENTATION AND EQUIPMENT

The probes that you will use today are:

- the **Stainless Steel temperature probe**
- the **pH probe** to evaluate acidity

Additional required equipment:

- Buret, buret clamp, and 1 volumetric pipet (25 mL) & bulb, 1-5 mL automatic pipet, magnetic stirrer, and microstirrer (or magnetic stirring bar).

The goals of this experiment will be i) to connect the probes to the interface; ii) to login to the laboratory computer network; iii) to locate and start the Logger Pro$^©$ program; iv) measure the temperature and/or pH of various solutions and conduct a titration; and v) explore the graphing and analysis capabilities of Logger Pro$^©$.

PROCEDURE

Chemical Hazards

- 0.2M Hydrochloric Acid: Toxic and Corrosive. May cause eye, skin, and respiratory tract irritation.
- 0.2M Sodium Hydroxide: Toxic and Corrosive. May cause eye, skin, and respiratory tract irritation.

Care should be taken when working with these reagents. Avoid inhalation and contact with skin, eyes, and clothing. Goggles, gloves, and lab coats are required at all times.

Setting Up the LabQuest© Application

1. Turn on and login to the computer. Your instructor will advise you of the proper procedures here.

2. Start the Logger Pro© application. When Logger Pro© starts, you'll see a lot of buttons in the top toolbar.

3. Connecting and Activating the Probes:
   a. Connect the Stainless Steel Temperature probe to CH1 of LabQuest©.
   b. Connect the USB cable to LabQuest©, and connect the USB cable to the computer.
   c. Restart Logger Pro© program. If your hardware has been successfully connected, you will see the LabQuest© status right below the toolbar. A Temperature vs. Time graph appears in the graph window. A green LED on LabQuest© shows you that it is connected. If the red LED is on, LabQuest© is not properly connected. Ask your instructor for advice. Note that power for LabQuest© is supplied by the USB port of the computer. It does not require auxiliary AC power or batteries.

4. Setup the Experiment Parameters:
   a. If it is necessary to change the range of the time scale (it should be 0~180 s). If you have to change the time scale, click the **Data Collection** button, and adjust the time scale.
   b. To add a title for the graph, pull down the Options menu, choose the Graph Options. In the Title box, input Temperature vs. Time, and click Done. Then you will see the title on the graph.

Part I—Temperature vs. Time

1. Click the [▶ Collect] button. The LabQuest© will collect data while plotting in the graph window. Then click the [■ Stop] button after about 120 seconds. The LabQuest© system has been recording the room temperature on your data spreadsheet and graphing the temperature as a function of time. To store your current run, pull down the **Experiment** menu and choose **Store Latest Run.** Select **Text Annotation** from the **Insert** menu on the toolbar. The pointer and the text box can be moved separately. Use this feature to label the data points you just collected as "Room Temperature".

Important: Whenever you get a useful run in the future experiments, you will often want to preserve it for comparison to subsequent runs. The runs will be stored as Run 1, Run 2, Run 3, etc. To store your current run, pull down the **Experiment** menu and choose **Store Latest Run.** This run will be preserved when you collect additional data. (Note: This action does **not,** however, save the data to disk. You do that using the **File** menu **Save** command.)

2. Put about 50 mL of tap water into a 250 mL beaker and insert the Temperature Probe into water. Click the [▶ Collect] button. The LabQuest© will collect data while plotting in the graph window. Then click the [■ Stop] button after about 120 seconds.

The LabQuest© has been recording the water temperature on the data spreadsheet. Label this second data set "Water Temperature" on the graph by using the **Text Annotation** feature. This time save the data by accessing the **File** menu and using the **Save** option.

This brings us to an important topic. How will you label your data files so you (and we) can determine who made them and what they contain? Here is how you'll do it: You and your partner have a unique login name (your locker #). Therefore, every file that you produce must start with that login name. On a given date, you will perform just one experiment. Thus, every file name should include the date so that the experiment is identified. Finally, you often will generate several files for a given experiment, so you should number them. This last number will not tell us exactly what the file contains, but it will give each file a unique name. So, for example, if you were working at station 41, using locker C41, on Sept. 29, and you produced your third data file for the day, you would name it:

C41_9-29_3

The underscores and dash are important for us to identify your work. If you lose track of your file numbers for that day and had already saved a file with that name, the program would state that the file already exists and ask whether to replace it. Since you don't want to overwrite your data files, choose **No** and then save under a name with a different file number. Once you have named the file, you must save it to the **My Documents** folder which appears on the C drive. For printing the graph for your group, pull down the **File** menu, choose **print graph,** mark **print footer** box, then input you and your partner's name at **Name** dialog box, and input your locker number in **Comment** dialog box. This is essential for you and your partner to distinguish your work from others in the class. Your names must appear on all graphs.

3. **Print** your Temp. vs. Time graph.

Part II—Temperature vs. Volume

1. For this next experiment, you will need to change the data collection mode from **Time Based** to **Events with Entry.** To generate a blank page, click the **New** button. To get the **Temperature vs. Volume** graph, click the **Data Collection** button, change the mode from **Time Based** to **Events with Entry.** Set the number of columns as 1. Set the **Column Name** box as **Volume** and the corresponding **unit** as mL. Press the **Done** button when ready. You will see a **Temperature vs. Volume** graph. Change the range of the volume to 150 mL—click the right end of volume axis and enter a value of 150. Similary, change the range of temperature to 0–65°C.

2. Obtain 25 mL of tap water using a graduated cylinder. Place the water in a 250 mL beaker.

3. Obtain 150 mL of tap water in a 250 mL beaker. Heat the water on a hot plate to about 80°C (check the temperature using your thermometer). Do not let the thermometer rest on the bottom of the glass beaker, you should check the temperature of the water in the middle of the solution. Your instructor will supply hot mitts to assist with removal of the beaker from the hot plate. You will add portions of the heated water to the room temperature water and monitor the temperature.

4. Insert the temperature probe into the 250 mL beaker filled with 25 mL of room temperature tap water. Click the ▶ Collect button and then the 🌀 Keep button. Enter the volume as 0.0 mL, the computer will record the corresponding temperature. Press **OK** to keep the data point.

5. Now measure 25 mL of hot water using a 50 mL graduated cylinder (be careful handling the hot water) and pour it into the cold water, stirring the mixture with a glass rod. Click the Keep button, enter the volume as 25.0 mL. Once again the computer will automatically record the corresponding temperature. Press OK to add the data point to your graph.

6. Repeat the procedure (measuring 25 mL hot water, mixing and recording) an additional four times, noting the corresponding combined values (50 mL, 75 mL, 100 mL, and 125 mL) with the appropriate number of significant figures.

7. Click the Stop button and title the graph **Temperature vs. Volume**. Use the **Autoscale** button to automatically adjust the scale on your graph. **Save** the data and **Print** the graph.

Part III—pH Measurements (I)

1. The next measurements to be made are temperature and pH (a measure of acidity) by adding a base to an acid. In 150 mL beakers obtain about 100 mL of 0.2M hydrochloric acid and about 120 mL of 0.2M sodium hydroxide.

2. Close the Logger Pro© program. While keeping the temperature probe at CH1, plug the pH probe at CH2 and restart the Logger Pro© program. Now you will see two graphs in the graph window. Change the time range to 60 seconds in both graphs using the button.

3. In a clean 250 mL beaker, place the temperature probe and pH meter into 50 mL of deionized water (measured with a graduated cylinder) in such a way that the probes do not touch each other. Using your 50 mL graduated cylinder, measure and add 50 mL of the hydrochloric acid solution to the water. Measure 60–70 mL of the 0.2M NaOH solution in your 100 mL graduated cylinder.

4. Begin collecting data by Collect button; data acquisition will begin. Slowly add the 60–70 mL of the sodium hydroxide solution. Try to add the sodium hydroxide at a roughly constant rate and over a time span of about 45 seconds. Agitate gently during the process. **DO NOT STIR BY USING pH PROBE AS A STIRRING ROD—use a glass stirring rod!** Stop the program when 60 seconds have elapsed. Make certain the scales are correct by using the **Autoscale** button on each graph. Title the graphs **pH vs. Time** and **Temperature vs. Time. Save** the data and name the file when prompted. **Print** the graphs—both graphs will print on the same page.

Part IV—pH Measurements (II)

1. Next you will conduct a titration of 0.2M HCl with 0.2M NaOH. Unplug the temperature probe at CH1, and connect the pH meter to channel CH1. Close the Logger Pro© program and reopen it. This time you will see how the pH meter works. This time in the graph window, you will get pH vs. Time. To get the pH vs. Volume graph, you have got to change the **data collection mode.** To do this, click the **Data Collection button** , change the mode from **Time based** to **Events with entry.** Set the **Number of Columns** as 1, the **column name** as **Volume,** and the corresponding **unit** is set as **mL.** Press **Done** button. Then you will see **pH vs. Volume.** Change the range of volume to 50 mL by just clicking the right end of the volume axis and enter the value 50.

Note: Normally you would calibrate the pH meter to assure accuracy. However, for this experiment, it will be sufficient to use the internal calibration already installed in the meter.

2. Prepare a buret for the titration. First clean the buret according to the method of Appendix III. Using a funnel, fill the buret to the zero mark at eye level with 0.2*M* NaOH. Place an empty beaker underneath the full buret when it is not in use in case of leaks.

3. Practice transferring a liquid between two beakers using a 25 mL volumetric pipet according to Appendix III (use water to practice). Ask your instructor to help you if necessary.

4. Measure (with a graduated cylinder) 25 mL of deionized water and add to a 250 mL beaker. Using your volumetric pipet, transfer 25 mL of 0.2*M* HCl to the 250 mL beaker.

5. Now you are ready to begin your titration. To conduct this experiment, you will add NaOH until the equivalence point (where moles of acid = moles of base) is reached and then past equivalence to a basic pH. For this titration, the equivalence point is reached at a pH of 7.0. Since the acid and base are equimolar (have the same concentration), this should theoretically occur when the volume of 0.2*M* NaOH added is precisely equal to that of the 0.2*M* HCl in the beaker (25 mL).

6. Place the beaker containing the HCl solution exactly on the center of the magnetic stirrer and under the buret. Attach a microstirrer to the pH probe (alternatively you can add a stirring bar to the beaker) and place the pH probe in the solution. Set the stirrer on the lowest setting. Click ▶ Collect button. *Before* you add any NaOH to HCl, click, enter the volume as 0.0, and click **OK**.

7. Add approximately 5 mL of NaOH from your buret and allow the pH reading to stabilize. Click 🌀 Keep and record the exact volume as indicated by the buret to the correct number of decimal places. Click **OK**. During your titration read the buret correctly and record the added volume of NaOH precisely and to the correct number of significant figures!

8. Add another 5 mL of NaOH, allow the pH reading to stabilize, click 🌀 Keep and record the exact volume from the buret. The volume recorded should be the additive volume, here approximately 10 mL. Click **OK** to record the value.

9. Repeat step 8 twice more, adding 5 mL at a time recording the pH and total additive volume until you have added 20 mL of NaOH.

10. Now record pH and volume readings at 1 mL increments, until reaching about 24 mL, each time recording the volume and pH.

11. At this point, the pH should be changing rapidly. Continue adding the NaOH a drop at at time, giving pH time to stabilize between each drop, until a pH of 7.0 is reached. Record the volume at pH 7.0 (it is not necessary to record the pH at every drop). If you overshoot this level, simply record the volume and pH closest to the equivalence point.

12. Record the pH at 26 mL, then record the volume and pH after each 1.0 mL addition of NaOH until 30 mL.

13. Complete the titration curve by recording the pH and exact volume at approximately 35, 40, 45, and 50 mL

14. Now click ◼ Stop . Change the title of the graph to **pH vs. Volume NaOH Added.** Add your name and your partner's name to the graph. **Save** the data, **Autoscale** and **Print** out the graph.

Part V—pH Measurements (III)

Now you will be introduced to the automatic pipet. This piece of equipment is very delicate, so please review Appendix III before use.

Some things to keep in mind as you use the automatic pipet:

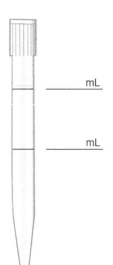

- NEVER lay the pipet on its side, always return the pipet to a pipet stand when not in use to avoid damage to the pipet.
- Practice using the pipet before performing the experiment; ask your instructor if you have any questions.
- Do not set volumes outside the pipet's volume range.

1. Read the instructions in Appendix III on using the automatic pipet and practice using the automatic pipet.

2. Note that a pipet tip has two reference marks to check your pipetting accuracy (Figure). Determine the volume corresponding to each mark. Show your results to your instructor before moving on.

3. Next you will conduct a titration of 0.2M HCl with 0.2M NaOH using an automatic pipet. Open a new document of your LoggerPro© software. In the graph window, you will get pH vs. Time. To get the pH vs. Volume graph, you have got to change the data collection mode. To do this, click the Data Collection button ▶ Collect , change the mode from Time based to Events with entry. Set the Number of Columns as 1, the column name as Volume, and the corresponding unit is set as mL. Press the Done button. Then you will see pH vs. Volume.

    Change the range of volume to 50 mL by just clicking the right end of the volume axis and enter the value 50.

4. Obtain approximately 75mL of 0.2M NaOH and approximately 30mL of HCl.

5. Measure (with a graduated cylinder) 25 mL of deionized water and add to a 250 mL beaker. Using your volumetric pipet, transfer 25 mL of 0.2M HCl to the 250 mL beaker.

6. Set your automatic pipet to 5.00 mL. Rinse a tip 2–3 times with NaOH, discarding these rinses in your waste beaker. Practice properly dispensing liquid from the pipet. Remember: NEVER lay the pipet on its side, return it to a pipet stand when not in use.

7. Now you are ready to begin your titration. To conduct this experiment, you will add NaOH until the equivalence point (where moles of acid equals the moles of base) is reached and then past equivalence to a basic pH. For this titration, the equivalence point is reached at a pH of 7.0. Since the acid and base are equimolar (have the same concentration), this should theoretically occur when the volume of 0.2M NaOH added is precisely equal to that of the 0.2M HCl in the beaker (25 mL).

8. Place the pH probe in the beaker containing the HCl solution. Click the collect button ▶ Collect . Before you add any NaOH to HCl, click 🌀 Keep , enter the volume as 0.0, and click OK.

9. Using your automatic pipet, add 5.00mL of NaOH to the HCl solution and allow the pH reading to stabilize. Click 🌀 Keep and record the exact volume as indicated by the automatic pipet to the correct number of decimal places. Click OK.

10. Add another 5 mL of NaOH, allow the pH reading to stabilize, click 🌀 Keep and record the exact volume from the automatic pipet. The volume recorded should be the additive volume, here approximately 10.00 mL. Click OK to record the value.

11. Repeat step 9 twice more, adding 5 mL at a time recording the pH and total additive volume until you have added 20 mL of NaOH.

12. Now record pH and volume readings at 1.00 mL increments, until reaching 30 mL, each time recording the volume and pH. Give the pH time to stabilize between each recording.

13. Complete the titration curve by recording the pH and exact volume at approximately 35, 40, 45, and 50 mL

14. Now click [Stop] . Change the title of the graph to pH vs. Volume NaOH Added with Pipet. Add your name and your partner's name to the graph. Save the data, Autoscale and Print out the graph.

Part VI—Curve Fitting and Manual Entry

There are a number of features to the spreadsheet and graphing functions that you need to become familiar with, including manual data input, curve fitting, and some basic data analysis skills. Follow the procedure below:

1. Detach the LabQuest$^©$ interface from the computer and close the program (make sure that you have saved all data).

2. Reopen the Logger Pro$^©$ program. You will see two columns labeled X and Y.

3. First choose **Column Options** by pulling down **Data** menu, click X. From **Column Definition** tile, change name from X to **Pressure,** Short name **P,** unit **torr.** Then click the **Options** tile, in **Displayed Precision,** change from **Automatic** to **3.** Press **Done** when ready. Then you will see column **X** have changed to **Pressure(torr)**

4. Then choose **Column Options** by Pulling down **Data** menu, click Y. From **Column Definition** tile, change name from **Y** to **Volume,** Short name **V,** unit **mL.** Then click the **Options** tile, in **Displayed Precision,** change from **Automatic** to **3.** Press **Done** when ready. Then you will see column **Y** has changed to **Volume(mL).**

5. Then you can input the following data manually by clicking the corresponding cell:

Pressure(torr)	Volume(mL)
400.000	42.600
500.000	34.100
600.000	28.400
700.000	24.300
800.000	21.300
900.000	18.900
1000.000	17.000
1100.000	15.500
1200.000	14.200

6. Click the **Autoscale** button; you will see a graph. Select the graph, choose **Graph Options** by pulling down the **Options** menu, in **graph options** tile, input the title as **Volume vs. Pressure,** from Appearance, and mark the **Point Protectors** checkbox. Click **Done** when ready. click button, at **General Equation** box, choose **A/P (inverse),** click **Try fit,** see if the curve fits the data. Then press **OK.**

7. Pull down the **Analyze** menu, choose **Interpolation Calculator,** to get the pressure value when the volume is 30.00 mL. **Autoscale** and **Print** the graph with this interpolated value showing. Close the auto fit box and the interpolation calculator.

8. Usually there is not much use of the data in this crude form. In fact, it is just a series of line segments that connect the data points (which is not useful). Let's improve this graph. In many experimental situations, we wish to manipulate the data until it shows a **linear** relationship (i.e., graphs as a straight line). We can convert our pressure-volume data to produce a straight-line graph. To do so, we will have to change the graph to **Volume vs. 1/Pressure.** Choose **New Calculated Column** by Pulling down **Data** menu. From **Column Definition** tile, name the column as **1/Pressure,** short name **1/P,** unit **1/torr.** In Equation, choose **Pressure** by pulling down **Variables (Columns),** then you will see in **Equation, Pressure** will emerge. Change **Pressure to 1/ "Pressure"** click the **Options** tile in **Displayed**

Precision, check the "significant figures" box and change precision from **3** to 6. Press Done when ready. Then you will see a new calculated column, **1/Pressure(1/torr)** appears.

9. Pull down the **Options** menu and choose **Graph Options.** Change the Title in Graph Options from Volume vs. Pressure to **Volume vs. 1/Pressure.**

10. On the graph, left click on the x axis label, you will be given the option to change your scale. Select 1/Pressure as your X axis. **Autoscale** your graph.

11. You will get a straight line. This time for curve fit, choose **Linear fit** button instead of **curve fit.** Again, use the "Interpolation Calculator" function to interpolate for the inverse pressure at a volume of 30.00 mL.

12. **Save,** and **print** out the graph showing the interpolation in same manner.

CLEANUP AND FINISHING UP

Rinse the pH probe with deionized water and replace its protective cover (if the solution has spilled from the protective cover, please notify your instructor so that it can be refilled; it is **not** water). Rinse the temperature probe with deionized water.

- Log out of your computer before shutting it down. Return your computer, LabQuest© and probes.
- Dispose of your solutions and other waste as directed by your instructor.
- Clean and put away your glassware.
- Clean up your lab bench.
- Lock your locker.

Staple and turn in your eight graphs with a coversheet, and have a nice day.

BEFORE YOU COME TO LAB YOU MUST COMPLETE A PRELAB ASSIGNMENT:

Experiment 5: Introduction to the LabQuest© Interface Online PRELAB Quiz:

- The Introduction to the LabQuest© Interface Online PRELAB Quiz is composed of multiple choice questions.
- The PRELAB score accounts for 40 points of your total lab score.
- The PRELAB quiz is timed, and it must be submitted before **11:59 pm the night before your experiment.**
- You may only submit the PRELAB quiz once.
- In order to prepare for your PRELAB quiz, it is recommended that you study the background information, calculations, and lab procedure for the experiment in your lab manual. You may be asked to perform calculations; the correct answer will need to be reported to the proper number of significant figures and with the appropriate units.
- You may be asked to prepare and print out a graph that you will turn into your instructors when you come to lab.

6

Back-Titration—Evaluation of Antacids

BACKGROUND

In this experiment, we will be evaluating the *effectiveness* of commercial antacids. Why do we use antacids? In digestion, your stomach produces acid, HCl(aq), which hydrolyzes starches to simple sugars (glucose). Sometimes your system is out of balance and produces too much acid. This common condition of too much acid can result in "heartburn."

Some people produce too much acid; individuals with this condition are called *hypersecretors*. Those who produce too little acid are *hyposecretors*. For hypersecretors, common ailments include duodenal ulcers (ulcers in the upper part of the small intestine) as well as gastric (stomach) ulcers and acid reflux (heartburn).

We can take at least two different actions to respond to this type of indigestion.

1. Take one of a group of relatively new drugs designed for treatment of ulcers, such as Tagamet, Zantec, etc., which act to suppress the production of acid by the stomach.

2. Take an antacid, which acts to neutralize excess stomach acid.
   We'll study this case!

Two types of bases are used in antacids:

1. Weak bases

$$CaCO_3 \qquad \text{carbonates } (CO_3^{2-})$$
$$NaHCO_3 \qquad \text{bicarbonates } (HCO_3^-)$$

2. Low-solubility strong bases

$$Mg(OH)_2 \qquad \text{magnesium hydroxide}$$
$$Al(OH)_3 \qquad \text{aluminum hydroxide}$$

Typical neutralization reaction:

(excess acid)

$$CO_3^{2-}(aq) + H_3O^+(aq) \rightarrow HCO_3^-(aq) + H_2O(l)$$

Typical antacids we are all familiar with include the following: $CaCO_3$ (Tums), $MgCO_3$ (used in buffered aspirin), $Mg(OH)_2$ (milk of magnesia), $Al(OH)_2NaCO_3$ (Rolaids), and $NaHCO_3$ (Alka-Seltzer). Representative reactions are shown below.

$$CaCO_3(s) + 2HCl(aq) \rightarrow CaCl_2(aq) + H_2O(l) + CO_2(g)$$

$$MgCO_3(s) + 2HCl(aq) \rightarrow MgCl_2(aq) + H_2O(l) + CO_2(g)$$

$$Mg(OH)_2(s) + 2HCl(aq) \rightarrow MgCl_2(aq) + H_2O(l)$$

$$Al(OH)_2 NaCO_3(s) + 4HCl(aq) \rightarrow AlCl_3(aq) + NaCl(aq) + 3H_2O(l) + CO_2(g)$$

$$NaHCO_3(aq) + HCl(aq) \rightarrow NaCl(aq) + H_2O(l) + CO_2(g)$$

$Al(OH)_3$ preparations vary in their solubility and neutralizing ability. $AlCl_3$ salt is formed in the neutralization reaction of gastric acid, which is insoluble and can lead to constipation.

$NaHCO_3$ is very soluble and fast reacting. It's used in baking soda and Alka-Seltzer. Its solubility allows for rapid absorption and removal from the gut. $NaHCO_3$ is not useful for long-term use and can cause systemic *alkalosis* and fluid retention. Alkalosis, the opposite of acidosis, results in excess base in the body fluids.

$CaCO_3$ is a very effective antacid that reacts more slowly than $NaHCO_3$ and is the active ingredient in Tums.

$Mg(OH)_2$, also known as milk of magnesia, is relatively insoluble and is therefore an antacid that lasts longer in the stomach. It is fast acting and only a small amount of Mg^{2+} is absorbed. Mg salts have a laxative effect. Mg- and Al-containing antacids work well together to offset their individual effect on bowel function and are used in preparations such as Mylanta and Maalox.

How can we determine the amount of base present in an antacid? We could dissolve a tablet to form a basic solution and then titrate with a standardized acid, but this approach has problems.

1. Antacids are not very soluble in water (though they are soluble in acids).

2. Antacids are usually weak bases that exhibit "buffering" capacity (resistance to pH change) while being titrated.

To overcome these problems, we "back-titrate."

Add a known but excess amount of strong acid to completely neutralize the antacid tablet. The base of the antacid is completely neutralized and a stoichiometric amount of strong acid is neutralized. We then titrate the remaining acid (excess) with standardized strong base and indirectly determine how much acid had reacted.

This approach solves the problems of buffering and poor dissolution while allowing for the use of a strong acid/strong base, which is the simplest type of titration.

A = moles of $HCl(aq)$ added to antacid

N = moles of $HCl(aq)$ neutralized

B = moles of $HCl(aq)$ remaining after antacid reaction

A − B = N

We could determine an equivalent number of moles of base in an antacid tablet. Because commercial antacids can contain more than one type of base, we evaluate their "effectiveness" for neutralizing $HCl(aq)$.

We can determine the mass effectiveness (E)

N = moles of HCl neutralized

W = mass of antacid, g

E = N/W

We can determine the cost effectiveness(C)

N = moles of HCl neutralized

P = price per tablet, ¢

C = N/P

Some antacids dissolve very slowly even in acidic solutions. You can heat the mixture, carefully bringing it to a boil in a controlled manner, to help them dissolve and you should allow sufficient time. Heating also drives off any dissolved CO_2 that may be present, which may interfere with the analysis. It is possible that some "filler" material will not dissolve at all. Once you are confident that the base has dissolved, you then can proceed with the analysis.

The indicator, bromophenol blue, is yellow in acidic solution. After reaction, your solution will still be acidic because you intended to add excess HCl(aq). If it doesn't turn yellow upon addition of the indicator, then you did not add enough HCl(aq).

If this is the case, you must repeat the experiment up to this point before proceeding. Make sure that you note the concentrations of the HCl(aq) and NaOH(aq) solutions that you use, the name of the antacid studied, and the price and number of tablets in the -container of the antacid studied.

PROCEDURE

Chemical Hazards

- *0.6M Hydrochloric Acid: Toxic. Corrosive. May cause eye, skin, and respiratory tract irritation.*
- *1.0M Sodium Hydroxide: Toxic. Corrosive. May cause eye, skin, and respiratory tract irritation.*
- *Bromophenol Blue: May cause eye, skin, and respiratory tract irritation.*

Care should be taken when working with these reagents. Avoid inhalation and contact with skin, eyes, and clothing. Goggles, gloves, and lab coats are required at all times.

The purpose of today's experiment is to assess the neutralization capacity of a brand name antacid and evaluate its effectiveness on the basis of its mass and its cost. The experiment will encompass completely neutralizing an antacid tablet and titrating the residual or excess acid by the process known as back-titration. The experiment will be run in triplicate.

Prepare all glassware by cleaning, following the procedures outlined in Appendix II. This applies to beakers, graduated cylinders, flasks, pipets, burets, etc.

Obtain three of the same brand antacid tablets from your instructor, noting on Data Sheet I the brand name, price, and number of tablets in the bottle.

Required volumetric glassware: 25 mL volumetric pipet, 50 mL buret.

Part I—Transfer of HCl(aq) with a Volumetric Pipet and Preparing the Buret

1. Using deionized water and a 25 mL volumetric pipet, practice your pipeting technique as described in Appendix III. Ask your instructor if you need help.

2. Obtain about 50 mL of 0.6 M HCl(aq) standardized solution in a clean, dry 150 mL beaker and record its molarity on Data Sheet 1.

3. Carefully clean and prepare a 25 mL pipet for transfer of 0.6*M* HCl(aq) by rinsing the clean pipet first with deionized water then with two 5 mL portions of 0.6*M*

HCl(aq). Pipet 25.00 mL of the HCl(aq) solution into a clean and dry 125 mL Erlenmeyer flask.

Part II—Back Titration of an Antacid

1. Using a 50 mL graduated cylinder, add approximately 40 mL of deionized water to the Erlenmeyer-flask from Part I containing the 25.00 mL of 0.6M HCl(aq). The purpose here is to increase the volume while the number of moles of acid remains unchanged.

2. Using a weighing boat (tare the balance) and an analytical balance, weigh the first of your three antacid tablets. Weigh the tablet to 0.001 g. Record the results on Data Sheet I.

3. Add the whole weighed tablet to the HCl(aq) solution in the Erlenmeyer flask and place the flask on a hotplate over moderate heat and bring to a boil in a controlled manner. Allow sufficient time to assure reaction of all the antacid. Boiling of 1–2 minutes should be enough time. Allow the solution to cool to room temperature.

4. Clean and prepare a buret to deliver 1.00M NaOH as per Appendix III. Obtain about 40 mL of the standardized NaOH solution in a clean, dry 150 mL beaker and record its molarity on Data Sheet 1. Fill your buret with the standardized NaOH solution and make certain to remove any bubbles trapped in the tip. Record the initial buret reading (to 0.02 mL) on Data Sheet I.

5. Add 10 drops of bromophenol blue indicator solution to the cooled mixture from step 3. The solution in the flask should be yellow at this point. If it is not yellow, it is likely that you did not measure the correct amount of acid initially and will have to *repeat the experiment up to this point*.

6. Back-titrate this solution with the standardized 1.00M NaOH to determine how much acid is in excess after the neutralization reaction. As the reaction approaches the titration end point, you will see flashes of purple color in the area where the NaOH enters the flask. You should slow the titration process to dropwise at this point so that you do not overshoot the end point. When the purple color remains for 15 seconds after thorough mixing, the titration is complete. Record the final buret reading on Data Sheet I.

7. Repeat the experiment with two additional trials if required.

Calculations

For Data Sheet I:

1. Record the mass of each antacid tablet.

2. Calculate the number of moles of HCl added to the tablet in each determination ($n_{HCli} = M_{HCl} \times V_{HCl}$). (Use the molarity on the bottle from the lab for M_{HCl}).   Eq. 6.1

3. Calculate the number of moles of NaOH required to back-titrate the excess HCl ($n_{NaOH} = M_{NaOH} \times V_{NaOH}$). (Use the molarity on the bottle from the lab for M_{NaOH}).
Eq. 6.2

4. Moles of HCl in excess equal the moles of NaOH required
($n_{NaOH} = n_{HCl, excess}$)   Eq. 6.3

5. Calculate the number of moles of HCl neutralized by a tablet
($n_{HCl, neutralized by tablet} = n_{HCli} - n_{HCl, excess}$).   Eq. 6.4

For Data Sheet II:

6. Calculate the *mass effectiveness*- the number of moles of HCl neutralized per gram of antacid:
(mass effectiveness = $n_{HCl, neutralized by tablet}$/mass of tablet, g).   Eq. 6.5

7. Calculate the cost effectiveness—the number of moles of HCl neutralized per price of antacid (in cents).

(cost effectiveness = $n_{HCl, \text{ neutralized by tablet}}$/price per tablet, ¢).   Eq. 6.6

SAMPLE CALCULATION

An antacid tablet was dissolved in 30.00mL of 0.500M HCl. The excess acid was back-titrated with exactly 9.25mL of 1.10M NaOH. The average weight of a tablet is 1.105g. The tablet came from a bottle of 200 tablets that cost $4.99.

a) Calculate the moles of HCl neutralized by the tablet.

b) Calculate the mass effectiveness of the antacid.

c) Calculate the cost effectiveness of the antacid.

---

a) Calculate the number of moles of HCl added to the tablet

A = (0.03000L)(0.500M) = 0.0150 mol

Calculate the number of moles of NaOH required to back-titrate the excess HCl

B = (0.00925L)(1.10M) = 0.010175 mol

Calculate the number of moles of HCl neutralized by the tablet

N = A − B = 0.0150 mol − 0.010175 mol = 4.825 × 10^{-3} mol = 4.8 × 10^{-3} mol

b) N = moles of HCl neutralized by tablet = 4.825 × 10^{-3} mol

W = mass of antacid = 1.105 g

E = N/W = 4.4 × 10^{-3} mol/g

c) N = moles of HCl neutralized by tablet = 4.825 × 10^{-3} mol

P = price per tablet, ¢

= ($4.99/bottle)(100¢/1$)(1 bottle/200 tablets) = 2.495 ¢

C = N/P = 1.9 × 10^{-3} mol/¢

DATA SHEET I

- Show a sample calculation for each type of calculated value.

brand of antacid _____

cost of antacid: $ _____ per _____ tablets

concentration of HCl solution _____

concentration of NaOH solution _____

	Trial		
	1	**2**	**3**
mass of tablet	_____	_____	_____
final buret reading	_____	_____	_____
initial buret reading	_____	_____	_____
volume of titrant	_____	_____	_____
moles of HCl added	_____	_____	_____
moles of NaOH required	_____	_____	_____
moles of HCl neutralized by tablet	_____	_____	_____

mean value, moles of HCl neutralized by tablet _____

DATA SHEET II

- Show a sample calculation for each type of calculated value.

	Trial		
Mass effectiveness (E)	**1**	**2**	**3**
N = moles of HCl neutralized			
W = mass of antacid			
E = N/W	_____	_____	_____
mean value		_____	
Cost effectiveness(C)			
N = moles of HCl neutralized			
P = price per tablet, ¢			
C = N/P	_____	_____	_____
mean value		_____	

Post-Laboratory Questions

1. Marble is predominantly calcium carbonate. Marble statues erode over time when exposed to acid rain. Give a brief chemical explanation for this occurrence, including a balanced chemical equation.

2. Given the five commercial products mentioned in the write-up, Tums, buffered aspirin, milk of magnesia, Rolaids, and Alka-Seltzer, which would you expect to be more effective on mass basis to neutralize stomach acid? Back up your reasoning with pertinent calculations.

3. The reaction of baking soda (NaHCO$_3$) and vinegar (CH$_3$COOH, acetic acid) are often used for demonstration of "chemical volcanoes". Write a balanced chemical equation to show what happens in the reaction.

BEFORE YOU COME TO LAB YOU MUST COMPLETE A PRELAB ASSIGNMENT:

Experiment 6: Back-Titration—Evaluation of Antacids Online PRELAB Quiz:

- The online Back-Titration PRELAB Quiz is composed of multiple choice questions.
- The PRELAB score accounts for 40 points of your total lab score.
- The prelab quiz is timed, and it must be submitted before **11:59 pm the night before your experiment.**
- You may only submit the PRELAB quiz once.
- In order to prepare for your PRELAB quiz, it is recommended that you study the background information, calculations, and lab procedure for the experiment in your lab manual. You may be asked to perform calculations; the correct answer will need to be reported to the proper number of significant figures and with the appropriate units.
- You may be asked to prepare and print out a graph that you will turn into your instructors when you come to lab.

Qualitative Analysis

HISTORY

The methods of qualitative analysis are as old as the science of chemistry. Qualitative analysis is used to identify and ultimately classify matter, usually in the form of compounds or elements. Early alchemists working in the Middle Ages (400–1450) learned a lot about matter using methods of trial-and-error. These ancient scholars developed procedures to manufacture different metal, glass, cloth and other useful materials. Along the way, methods of drying, distillation (separation and purification by boiling point), and crystallization (separation and purification by freezing point) were developed to make substances as pure as possible.

The modern subject of chemistry did not begin to appear until the 18th century. At that time it was recognized that the study of the nature of matter should be conducted based on a specified set of rules. The early chemists included Robert Boyle (1627–1691), who devised a set of rules for chemical experimentation; Jons Jakob Berzelius (1779–1848), who gave us early chemical symbols, determined atomic weights and discovered several new elements; John Dalton (1766–1844), who proposed the first theory of the atom; and Antoine-Laurent Lavoisier (1743–1794), who first understood combustion and established a system of chemical terminology and who is considered the father of modern chemistry.

BACKGROUND INFORMATION

Most qualitative analysis was done at the lab bench using test tubes, beakers, centrifuges, funnels, droppers, etc. This type of analysis has been called "wet chemistry" and to a great extent has been replaced by sophisticated instruments that are more sensitive, more accurate and more efficient than the old bench-top studies. As a learning tool, the bench-top wet chemistry methods must be learned by any serious student of chemistry.

We know that every compound or element has a unique set of chemical and physical properties that we can use to identify, differentiate and classify components of the mixture. Classical methodology can employ several simple steps in which basic information can be gained quickly. For example, heating the sample may yield smoke or char indicating the presence of carbon, or moisture could be released indicating the presence of water. Simple flame tests can be used to discover the presence of specific elements or compounds by virtue of the flame color. Having conducted these preliminary tests, the next series of steps is usually preceded by dissolution of the unknown sample in water.

If the unknown is a mixture, often it's necessary to separate the components during the identification process. In qualitative analysis procedures, the chemical properties of an unknown material are determined by systematically exposing the unknown to number of reagents and observing the results. Covalent compounds (compounds in which electrons are shared) can be identified by comparing their physical properties such as boiling point or refractive index. Ionic compounds (compounds in which electrons are transferred) are more easily identified with their chemical properties. Our discussion will be limited to inorganic compounds which are primarily ionic in chemical character.

In this experiment, mixtures will consist of ionic compounds; we will identify the positive ions or **cations**. We won't identify the negative ions or **anions**. We'll study mixtures of compounds containing silver (Ag^+), copper(II) (Cu^{2+}), and iron(III) (Fe^{3+}).

When ionic compounds are dissolved in water, the result is an aqueous solution containing the cations and anions of the dissolved compounds. When two such solutions are mixed, if no visible reaction occurs (i.e., no precipitate formation or color change), then we assume that all of the cation-anion combinations are soluble in the solution. Otherwise, if a reaction does occur, it is upon us to determine the ions involved.

If a solid precipitate forms upon addition of a reagent, this would indicate the presence of a particular cation in the unknown. To separate the precipitate from the balance of the solution, we can employ **filtration, centrifugation** or **decantation**. Filtration utilizes a filter medium (usually filter paper) to separate the solid from the liquid. Centrifugation uses centrifugal force for separation of mixtures. The more dense components of the mixture migrate away from the axis of the centrifuge while the less dense components migrate towards the axis. The solution which lies above the solid and is called the **supernate**, is simply poured (decanted) off leaving the solid behind.

There are three different types of chemical equations that are frequently used to describe the reactions in aqueous media. Let us examine the reaction of silver nitrate, $AgNO_3$, and hydrochloric acid, $HCl(aq)$, in water. Mixing solutions of $AgNO_3$ and $HCl(aq)$ results in the formation of white solid, $AgCl(s, white)$. The **molecular chemical equation** for a reaction is one where all reagent and product species are present in their undissociated forms. The molecular equation for this reaction is given as:

$$AgNO_3\ (aq) + HCl(aq) \rightarrow HNO_3(aq) + AgCl(s, white)$$

The labels (aq) and (s) refer to the physical state of the species. An aqueous ion is given the label (aq), a solid the label (s), a liquid is denoted by the label (l), and gases are labeled as (g). Note that water, although present, is not directly involved in the chemical reaction; instead, water's presence is felt in the aqueous nature of the three non-solid species. Furthermore, it is not always necessary to indicate the color of the species involved. However, in the cases where the nature of the chemical reaction can be determined from color, then it is often supplied.

Next, let us discuss the **total** or **complete ionic equation.** This equation is the same as the molecular chemical equation, except that all aqueous species are given in their dissociated form. (For example, instead of $KNO_3\ (aq)$, write $K^+\ (aq) + NO_3^-\ (aq)$). For the same reaction as previously mentioned we would write the complete ionic equation as:

$$Ag^+(aq) + NO_3^-(aq) + H^+(aq) + Cl^-(aq) \rightarrow H^+(aq) + NO_3^-(aq) + AgCl(s, white)$$

Notice that the H^+ and NO_3^- ions are present as both reactants and products in the above reaction. These ions that are not directly involved in the reaction are called **spectator ions.** We can now write a chemical reaction dealing with *only* the ions that are directly involved in the chemical reaction, the **net ionic equation.** Here we rewrite the complete ionic equation neglecting all of the spectator ions:

$$Ag^+(aq) + Cl^-(aq) \rightarrow AgCl(s, \text{white})$$

Most of the time, it will suffice to provide the net ionic equation. This type of equation provides us with all the pertinent information regarding the transformations that we will be observing.

Another reaction used in qualitative analysis is the **complexation reaction.** In this process a chemical species called a **complex ion** or **neutral complex** is formed, resulting in a distinct color change. Complex formation usually occurs when a transition metal ion, such as iron(III) or copper(II), combines with either an anion or a polar neutral molecule, such as water (H_2O) or ammonia (NH_3). These complexing agents that attach themselves to the transition metal ion are called **ligands.** Complex reactions are balanced differently since the complex ion forms only in solution and is not a neutral compound. Complex ions also use a different naming system that is beyond the scope of this course.

We'll use thiocyanate (SCN^-) and ammonia (NH_3) as complexing agents (ligands) in this experiment. Thiocyanate forms a complex with iron(III) called thiocyanatoiron(III) ion with the formula $[FeSCN]^{2+}$(aq). The complex forms red solutions and is commonly used to indicate the presence of iron(III) ion. We'll use ammonia to indicate the presence of copper(II). Ammonia and copper(II) combine to form the brilliant blue solution of the complex tetraamminecopper(II) ion with the formula $[Cu(NH_3)_4]^{2+}$(aq).

Analysis of Solutions Containing Silver(I), Copper(II) and Iron(III) Cations.

In this experiment we will be working with the nitrate solutions of silver, copper(II), and iron(III). You will investigate the reactions of $AgNO_3$, $Cu(NO_3)_2$, and $Fe(NO_3)_3$, with aqueous solutions of hydrochloric acid (HCl(aq)), sodium hydroxide (NaOH(aq)), ammonium hydroxide (NH_4OH(aq)), sulfuric acid (H_2SO_4(aq)), and potassium thiocyanate (KSCN(aq)). You will characterize the reactions that do occur by providing the net ionic equations.

After the behavior of these metal solutions with the test solutions have been fully characterized, you will perform the same set of tests on a mixture containing all three of the metal cations. Do solutions of multiple cations behave the same? Finally, you will be provided with a solution of unknown composition that will contain one or more of the metals surveyed in this experiment. It will be up to you to determine which of the metals are present in your given unknown.

PURPOSE

1. Learn the behavior of metal cation solutions with various reagents.
2. Develop your ability to describe chemical observations with net ionic equations and your observations.
3. Perform a Qualitative Analysis on a solution containing an unknown mixture of metal cations.

INSTRUMENTATION AND EQUIPMENT

No sophisticated instrumentation or apparatus is involved in this experiment.

Chemical Hazards

- 0.1M Silver Nitrate: Toxic. May cause eye, skin, and respiratory tract irritation.
- 0.1M Copper(II) Nitrate: Toxic. Oxidant. May cause eye, skin, and respiratory tract irritation.
- 0.1M Iron(III) Nitrate: Oxidant. May cause eye, skin, and respiratory tract irritation.
- 6M Hydrochloric Acid: Toxic and Corrosive. May cause eye, skin, and respiratory tract irritation.
- 6M Sodium Hydroxide: Toxic and Corrosive. May cause eye, skin, and respiratory tract irritation.
- 6M Ammonium Hydroxide: Toxic and Corrosive. May cause eye, skin, and respiratory tract irritation. Volatile: Harmful by inhalation.
- 6M Sulfuric Acid: Toxic and Corrosive. May cause eye, skin, and respiratory tract irritation.
- 0.1M Potassium Thiocyanate: Toxic. May cause eye, skin, and respiratory tract irritation.

Care should be taken when working with these reagents. Avoid inhalation and contact with skin, eyes, and clothing. Goggles, gloves, and lab coats are required at all times. If accidentally ingested, contact poison control immediately.

PROCEDURE

This procedure should be followed carefully and your observations should be documented precisely on the prepared data sheets. Any trials in this experiment with suspicious results should be repeated.

Labeling your Glassware

We will now prepare labels for 7 test tubes and 1 beaker. Label the test tubes 1–7. Attach these labels firmly to seven test tubes that have been cleaned well. Last, prepare a label for your waste beaker. Write "Waste" on the label and firmly affix it to a 600mL beaker or your largest beaker if you do not have a 600mL beaker.

Part I—Studying Reactions of the Ag^+ Ion

1. **Before beginning**, use a clean 10mL graduated cylinder to measure 2mL of deionized water. Add the 2mL of water to test tube 1. Using a small piece of tape mark the level of 2mL of solution in your test tube. Now pour out the water and dry the test tube. Filling the test tube to the tape mark will give approximately 2mL of solution. Repeat this process with test tubes 2 through 7.

2. Obtain 2.0mL of 0.1M $AgNO_3$ in the test tube labeled #1.

3. Follow the next steps carefully and note your observations on your data sheets.
   a. Add 8 drops of 6M HCl(aq) to the $AgNO_3$ solution in test tube #1. Thoroughly mix the solution with a clean glass rod in the test tube. Record your observations.

   b. Add 1mL of the 6*M* NH_4OH solution to the tube. Thoroughly mix the contents and record your observations.

   c. Add 15 drops of 6*M* HCl(aq) solution to the reaction mixture. (You may observe the tube heat up due to acid-base neutralization). Mix the solution thoroughly and record your observations.

4. Obtain 2.0mL of 0.1M $AgNO_3$ in the test tube labeled #2.

   a. Add 15 drops 0.1M KSCN to the solution in test tube #2. Mix the solution thoroughly and record your observations.

5. Discard the contents of test tubes #1 and #2 into the "waste" beaker. Rinse the test tube using the method as described for the graduated cylinder in Part V (1).

Part II—Studying Reactions of the Cu^{2+} Ion

1. Obtain 2.0mL of 0.1*M* $Cu(NO_3)_2$ in the test tube labeled #3.

2. Follow the next steps carefully and note your observations on your data sheets.

   a. Add 8 drops of 6*M* HCl(aq) to the $Cu(NO_3)_2$ solution in test tube #3. Thoroughly mix the solution in the test tube. Record your observations.

   b. Add about 8 drops of the 6*M* NaOH solution to the solution. Thoroughly mix the contents and check the pH with pH paper and, if not basic, add NaOH dropwise until slightly basic. Record your observations. Immerse your stirring rod into the solution, and then touch the stirring rod to pH paper. The color of the solution on the pH paper will determine the pH of the solution. A basic solution will have a dark green or blue color on pH paper.

   c. Add 15 drops of 6*M* H_2SO_4(aq) solution to the reaction mixture. (You may observe the tube heat up due to acid-base neutralization). Mix the solution thoroughly and record your observations.

   d. Add 1mL of the 6*M* NH_4OH solution to the reaction mixture. Thoroughly mix the contents and record your observations.

3. Discard the contents of test tube #3 into the "waste" beaker. Rinse the test tube using the method as described for the graduated cylinder in Part V (1).

Part III—Studying Reactions of the Fe^{3+} Ion

1. Obtain 2.0mL of 0.1*M* $Fe(NO_3)_3$ in the test tube labeled #4.

2. Follow the next steps carefully and note your observations on your data sheets.

   a. Add 8 drops of 6*M* HCl(aq) to the $Fe(NO_3)_3$ solution in test tube #4. Thoroughly mix the solution in the test tube using a clean glass rod. Record your observations.

   b. Add about 8 drops of the 6*M* NaOH solution to the solution. Thoroughly mix the contents and check the pH with pH paper and, if not basic, add NaOH dropwise until slightly basic. Check the pH by touching the glass rod to the pH paper. Record your observations.

   c. Add 6 drops of 6*M* H_2SO_4 until the solution is slightly acidic, mix thoroughly, and observe your results. Use the pH paper and glass rod as above to adjust the pH.

   d. Add 6 drops of 6M NH_4OH to the solution. Thoroughly mix the contents and record your observations.

   e. Add 6 drops of 6*M* H_2SO_4 until the solution is slightly acidic, mix thoroughly, and observe your results. Use the pH paper and glass rod as above to adjust the pH.

   f. Add 5 drops of 0.1*M* KSCN solution, thoroughly mix the contents, and record your observations.

3. Discard the contents of test tube #4 into the "waste" beaker. Rinse the test tube as described for the graduated cylinder in Part V (1).

Part IV—Assaying a Mixture of Metal Cations in Solution

1. A 0.1M mixture of all three cations (Ag^+, Cu^{2+}, and Fe^{3+}) has been prepared and placed in the hood. Pour 2.0mL of this new mixture into the three clean labeled test tubes #5, #6, and #7.

2. Follow the next steps carefully and note your observations on your data sheets.
   a. Add 15 drops of the 6*M* HCl solution to the solution in test tube #5. Thoroughly mix the contents and record your observations.
   b. Add 3mL of the 6*M* NH_4OH solution to tube #6. Thoroughly mix the contents, wait 5 minutes, and record your observations.
   c. Add 3mL of 0.1*M* KSCN to the solution to tube #7. Thoroughly mix the solution in the test tube. Record your observations.

3. Discard the contents of test tubes #5, #6, and #7 into the "waste" beaker. Rinse these test tubes as described for the graduated cylinder in Part V (1).

Part V—Assaying a Solution Containing an Unknown Mixture of Cations

1. Thoroughly clean a 10mL graduated cylinder. Rinse twice with tap water (these rinses should be discarded into your waste beaker), and twice with deionized water.

2. In your clean 10mL graduated cylinder obtain 8.0mL of an unknown mixture provided by your laboratory instructor. Carefully record the code number of the unknown if provided.

3. Based on Parts I–IV of the experiment so far, devise a procedure for confirming the presence of Ag^+, Cu^{2+}, and/or Fe^{3+} in this unknown sample. Write the procedure on the data sheet after the list of reagents. A typical format would look like:

Procedure	**Observations**
1. First, ...	1. After adding, the solution . . . . . .
2.	
3.	

4. In the results section of this part of your data sheet, provide the identities of the ions present in your unknown solution. Provide the evidence upon which this determination was founded. Provide net ionic equations for each reaction observed.

Clean Up and Safety

Carefully clean all the glassware that was used in this experiment. Discard the chemical waste (including the first couple of rinses) in the "waste" beaker as described by your laboratory instructor.

   Wash your hands thoroughly with detergent or soap before you leave the laboratory.

DATA SHEET I

In this experiment we will use a laboratory journal format for our data. Please prepare your journal sheets before arriving at the lab. Proper preparation will be part of your grade in this experiment. Do not neglect this component.

On the following page is a sample data sheet for the first part of the experiment. You will create data sheets for parts I–V of the experiment (data sheet V is for the unknown). These data sheets will be checked by your instructor upon entry to the lab. Each individual person is responsible for completing and bringing his or her own set of data sheets. The "observations" section is for recording observations of each reaction. Was there a color change? A precipitate formation? Was heat evolved in the reaction? Etc. Record your observations before and after the addition of each reagent.

In the "results" section you will record the net ionic equation for any reaction that do occur. If no reaction occurs, indicate this by simply writing "no reaction."

SAMPLE DATA SHEET (DO NOT SUBMIT)

Experiment Name: Exp. 7: Qualitative Analysis

PART I: Studying the Reactions of the Ag^+ Ion:

Reagents	Amount	Concentration	Cautions
$AgNO_3$	4mL	0.1M	Toxic, irritant
HCl(aq)	8 drops + 15 drops	6M	Toxic, irritant
NH_4OH	1mL	6M	Toxic, corrosive, volatile, irritant
KSCN	15 drops	0.1M	Toxic, irritant

Observations

Reaction:	Observations:
2mL 0.1M $AgNO_3$ + 8 drops 6M HCl(aq)	
+ 1mL 6M NH_4OH	
+ 15 drops 6M HCl(aq)	
2mL 0.1M $AgNO_3$ + 15 drops 0.1M KSCN	

Results

Reaction:	Balanced net ionic equation:
2mL 0.1M $AgNO_3$ + 8 drops 6M HCl(aq)	
+ 1mL 6M NH_4OH	
+ 15 drops 6M HCl(aq)	
+ 15 drops 0.1M KSCN	

Additional Observations/Results:

Post-Laboratory Assignment

1. Provide a detailed analysis of the assay you performed in Part V of the experiment. How did you confirm the presence of each ion?

2. Qualitative Analysis Scheme

known solution	reagent added	observation
Ag^+(aq), NO_3^-(aq)	6M HCl(aq)	White precipitate, AgCl(s)
AgCl(s)	6M NH_4OH(aq)	Precipitate dissolves and complex forms, $Ag(NH_3)_2^+$(aq)
$Ag(NH_3)_2^+$(aq)	6M HCl(aq)	White precipitate, AgCl(s) confirms presence of Ag^+(aq)
Ag^+(aq), NO_3^-(aq)	0.1M KSCN	White precipitate, AgSCN(s)
Fe^{3+}(aq), NO_3^-(aq)	6M HCl(aq)	No reaction, Fe^{3+}(aq)
Fe^{3+}(aq), NO_3^-(aq)	6M NaOH(aq)	Rust colored precipitate, $Fe(OH)_3$(s)
$Fe(OH)_3$(s)	6M H_2SO_4(aq)	Re-dissolve precipitate, Fe^{3+}(aq)
Fe^{3+}(aq), SO_4^{2-}(aq)	6M NH_4OH(aq)	Rust colored precipitate, $Fe(OH)_3$(s)
$Fe(OH)_3$(s)	6M H_2SO_4(aq)	Re-dissolve precipitate, Fe^{3+}(aq)
Fe^{3+}(aq), SO_4^{2-}(aq)	0.1M KSCN	Red complex ion, $FeSCN^{2+}$(aq) confirms presence of Fe^{3+}
Cu^{2+}(aq), NO_3^-(aq)	6M HCl(aq)	No reaction, Cu^{2+}(aq)
Cu^{2+}(aq), NO_3^-(aq)	6M NaOH(aq)	Light blue precipitate, $Cu(OH)_2$(s)
$Cu(OH)_2$(s)	6M H_2SO_4(aq)	Precipitate dissolves, Cu^{2+}(aq)
Cu^{2+}(aq), SO_4^{2-}(aq)	6M NH_4OH(aq)	Brilliant blue complex ion, $Cu(NH_3)_4^{2+}$(aq) confirms the presence of Cu^{2+}

3. Construct a flow diagram for the separation of the three cations, Ag^+, Cu^{2+} and Fe^{3+} using the blank flow diagram below based on your experimental data base and the preceding qualitative analytical scheme. To separate precipitated solids you will centrifuge the solution. This will allow you to decant the solution above the precipitate for further analysis. The solution above the solid precipitate is called the supernatant.

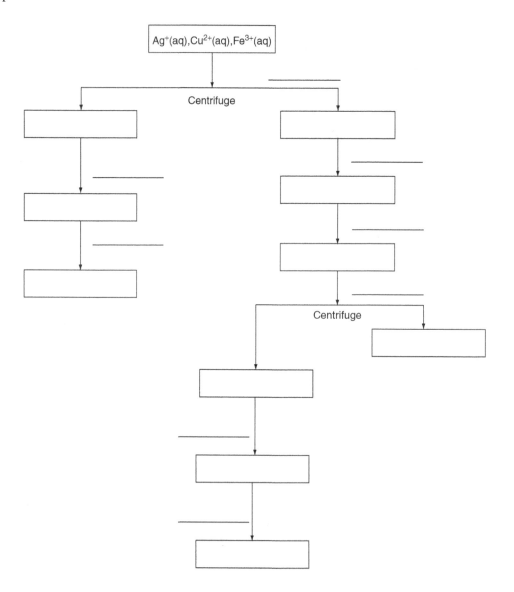

4. In a Breathalyzer test, the presence of alcohol (C_2H_5OH) in breath is detected by the following reaction as the color changes from reddish orange to green:

$$2K_2Cr_2O_7(aq) + 8H_2SO_4(aq) + 3C_2H_5OH(aq) \rightarrow 2Cr_2(SO_4)_3\,(aq) + 11H_2O(l) + 2K_2SO_4(aq) + 3CH_3COOH(aq)$$

What type of reaction is it? Explain.

BEFORE YOU COME TO LAB YOU MUST COMPLETE A PRELAB ASSIGNMENT:

Experiment 7: Qualitative Analysis Online PRELAB Quiz:

- The Qualitative Analysis Online PRELAB Quiz is composed of multiple choice questions.
- The PRELAB score accounts for 40 points of your total lab score.
- The PRELAB quiz is timed, and it must be submitted before **11:59pm the night before your experiment.**
- You may only submit the PRELAB quiz once.
- In order to prepare for your PRELAB quiz, it is recommended that you study the background information, calculations, and lab procedure for the experiment in your lab manual. You may be asked to perform calculations; the correct answer will need to be reported to the proper number of significant figures and with the appropriate units.

You must prepare and print out your data sheets for parts I–V as described in the DATA SHEET section. These will be collected from each individual by your instructors in lab.

8

Chemistry and Thermodynamics

BACKGROUND INFORMATION

Thermochemistry

All chemical reactions involve an energy change. Energy is how to measure the transfer of heat or capacity to do work. Some reactions **lose** energy (energy is released) while others **gain** energy (energy is absorbed). Energy considerations play an important role in determining whether or not a reaction will take place. Measurement of energy changes allows the ability to make predictions about chemical reactions.

The direction that energy flows determines the sign of the energy change. Energy flow is between the system and the surroundings. The system and the surroundings comprise the universe. Since energy is neither created nor destroyed, the total energy in the universe does not change. The study of heat flows is called **thermodynamics** and when chemical reactions are involved, the study is called thermochemistry. While energy forms may change (potential to kinetic energy), in any process energy is conserved. This is the **first law of thermodynamics.** In any thermodynamic analysis, a calculation of the change in any thermodynamic value equals the final value minus the initial value.

Energy is exchanged between the system and the surroundings in two ways:

HEAT (q) and WORK (w)

Heat amounts are determined through relation to **temperature,** where heat always flow from a higher to a lower temperature. **Work** calculations require being given appropriate data; w = F × d (work = force × distance through which force is applied.) In this experiment, measurement of the amount of heat released as an acid-base neutralization reaction takes place, under constant pressure (atmospheric pressure). The heat exchanged at constant pressure is defined to be ΔH, **the change in enthalpy.** ΔH is a measure of heat exchange per mole of reactant and has the units of kilo joules per mole. Enthalpy is an example of a **state function,** a thermodynamic quantity dependent only on its current state and not by how it got to that state. A change in any thermodynamic quantity is calculated by subtracting the initial value from the final.

$$\text{System} + \text{Surroundings} = \text{Universe} \qquad \text{Eq. 8.1}$$

When a chemical reaction liberates heat, which generally goes into the surroundings, we say the reaction is **exothermic.** $\Delta H < 0$; since the system has less enthalpy than it had before the reaction, the change in enthalpy is negative. When a chemical reaction absorbs heat from the surroundings, it has more enthalpy than it had before the reaction; the change in enthalpy is positive. $\Delta H > 0$; this is an **endothermic reaction**.

Energy can be transformed from one form to another, and all forms can be expressed by the same unit. The SI unit of energy is Joule, J where $1J = 1$ kg-m^2/s^2.

Calorimetry

By carrying out the reaction in an insulated container called a **calorimeter,** no heat escapes and all heat is evolved or absorbed. This heat will simply change the temperature of the contents of the calorimeter. The calorimeter is constructed of a material of very low thermal conductivity, is a good insulator, and absorbs only a small amount of heat. It is still necessary to determine $q_{calorimeter}$ or how much heat is absorbed by the calorimeter for any accurate determination of energy transfer.

Assume the system to be the calorimeter and its contents then:

$$q_{system} = q_{solution} + q_{calorimeter} + q_{reaction} = 0 \qquad \text{Eq. 8.2}$$

In this case the system is made of three components: the solution, the reaction and the calorimeter. We assume that heat is exchanged only **within** the system and not with the surroundings, so the change in the heat of the system is zero. For constant-pressure calorimetry, the heat exchanged in the reaction is equal to the change in enthalpy: $q_{rxn} = \Delta H$.

$$\Delta H = -(q_{solution} + q_{calorimeter}) \qquad \text{Eq. 8.3}$$

To determine q_{cal}, a simple experiment is preformed in the calorimeter. Accurately measure two quantities of water, one hot and one cold. Monitor the temperature of both and mix them in the calorimeter. The hot water will lose heat, while the cold water will gain heat. A perfect calorimeter would absorb no heat—all the heat from the hot water would transfer to the cold. But the calorimeter isn't perfect and will absorb a small amount of heat q_{cal}. Therefore, in this experiment, our system is made up of three components: the heat lost by the hot water (q_{hot}), the heat gained by the cold water (q_{cold}), and the heat absorbed by the calorimeter (q_{cal}).

$$q_{sys} = 0 = q_{hot} + q_{cold} + q_{cal}$$

Heat flow in or out of a system, q is described by the equation

$$q = mc \, \Delta T \qquad \text{Eq. 8.4}$$

where

$$m = \text{mass, g}$$

$$c = \text{specific heat, joules/g°C}$$

$$\Delta T = T_{final} - T_{initial}, \text{°C}$$

The value of c, the specific heat, is the amount of energy required to raise one gram of substance one degree Celsius. This is a tabulated value equal to 4.184 J/g°C for water.

Here q_{hot} represents the heat lost by the hot water ($q_{hot} = m_{hot}c_{water}\Delta T_{hot}$), and q_{cold} represents the heat gained by the cold water ($q_{cold} = m_{cold}c_{water}\Delta T_{cold}$). Because heat is lost by the hot water, q_{hot} will be negative. Conversely q_{cold} will be positive as the cold water increases in temperature. The amount of heat lost by the hot water will be greater in magnitude than the heat absorbed by the cold water because the calorimeter also absorbs some of the heat lost by the hot water. Therefore $(q_{hot} + q_{cold})$ will be a negative value. There is no chemical reaction in the mixing of hot and cold water so $\Delta H = 0$. Then

$$q_{sys} = 0 = q_{hot} + q_{cold} + q_{cal}$$
$$q_{cal} = -(q_{hot} + q_{cold}) \qquad \text{Eq. 8.5}$$

Having determined q_{cal}, where $q_{cal} = -(q_{hot} + q_{cold}) = m_{cal}c_{cal}\,\Delta T$, we can then establish C_{cal} the heat capacity of the calorimeter or the calorimeter constant. Note that because the value of $(q_{hot} + q_{cold})$ is negative, the value for q_{cal} should be positive. Since the mass and specific heat of the calorimeter are constant, their product, C_{cal} is also a constant.

$$\text{Then } q_{cal} = C_{cal}\,\Delta T = m_{cal}c_{cal}\,\Delta T \qquad \text{Eq. 8.6}$$

Once C_{cal} is established, it can be used in subsequent measurements of enthalpy by determining the ΔT. A series of experiments have been designed to measure several important thermochemical properties. These include the specific heat of a metal, the heat of solution for an ionic salt dissolved in water, and the heat of reaction for an acid-base neutralization. Precise measurement of reactant volumes and temperatures are essential for good results. A graphical extrapolation method is used to determine the required temperatures.

The Law of Dulong and Petit (and Einstein)—The Molar Heat Capacity of Copper

In 1819, the scientists Pierre Dulong and Alexis Petit noticed that the molar heat capacities of all metals were nearly the same averaging $\sim$25 J/mol°C. While they had no good explanation for this phenomenon, they used this observation to estimate atomic masses of metals. It wasn't until 1907 when Einstein showed that the molar heat capacities of metals at absolute zero (0 K) equaled the value of 3R where R is 8.314 J/mol K, the universal gas constant. In the analysis, Einstein treated the metal atoms as oscillators vibrating in three dimensions. An experiment is described below to measure the specific heat of copper through calorimetry.

In this experiment, we weigh out some copper and heat it to 100°C by placing it in a beaker of boiling water. We then transfer the copper to a measured volume of water in the calorimeter and monitor its temperature increase. The hot metal will transfer its thermal energy to the water and the calorimeter. In this case, the system is made of three components that exchange heat: the calorimeter (q_{cal}), the water (q_{water}), and the copper (q_{copper}). The equation that applies is

$$q_{sys} = q_{water} + q_{copper} + q_{cal} = 0$$

$$q_{cal} = -(q_{water} + q_{copper})$$

$$q_{metal} = m_{metal}c_{metal}\Delta T_{metal} \quad \text{where} \quad \Delta T_{metal} = T_{final} - T_{initial}\,,\,°C;$$
$$T_{initial} = 100°C$$

$$q_{water} = m_{water}c_{water}\Delta T_{water} \quad \text{where} \quad \Delta T_{water} = T_{final} - T_{initial}\,,\,°C;$$
$$(T_{final})_{metal} = (T_{final})_{water}$$

$$q_{cal} = C_{cal}\Delta T_{water}$$

The only unknown is the specific heat of the metal. A graphical extrapolation method is used to determine the required ΔTs. From this data, both the specific heat and molar heat capacity are calculated. The detailed procedure is described in the procedure section.

Enthalpy of Neutralization

The heat released in an acid-base neutralization (an exothermic reaction) carried out in a calorimeter will raise the temperature of the contents of the calorimeter. The acid-base reaction for HCl(*aq*) and NaOH(*aq*) can be represented by the net ionic equation:

$$H^+(aq) + OH^-(aq) \rightarrow H_2O(l) + \Delta \; (\Delta = \text{heat})$$

Using the stoichiometry of the neutralization reaction, the molar enthalpy can be determined. Once again, a graphical extrapolation method is used to determine the required ΔT's.

PURPOSE

The purpose of this experiment is to understand the concept of energy flows in chemical and physical reactions. Thermochemical measurements will include determination of the calorimeter constant, the molar heat capacity of copper, the heat of solution for ammonium nitrate, and the enthalpy of neutralization for the reaction of a strong acid and a strong base. The experiment will be conducted using the LabQuest© interface and Logger Pro© software.

Today's experiment includes:

- Determination of the calorimeter constant of the calorimeter (1or 2 graphs).
- Determination of the specific heat and molar heat capacity of copper (1 graph).
- Determination of the heat of solution of ammonium nitrate (1 graph).
- Determination of the molar enthalpy of neutralization (1graph).

Based on the results, you will also need to do some calculations (Data Sheets 1–4) and the post-lab section of the experiment.

INSTRUMENTATION AND EQUIPMENT

The instrumentation that you need in this lab will be:
- LabQuest© interface.
- 2 temperature probes.
- 1 calorimeter (2 nested polystyrene cups with cardboard cover).
- 1 additional polystyrene cup.

PROCEDURE

Chemical Hazards
- Ammonium Nitrate: Oxidizer. May cause eye, skin, and respiratory tract irritation.
- 2M Hydrochloric Acid: Toxic. Corrosive. May cause eye, skin, and respiratory tract irritation.
- 1M Sulfuric Acid: Toxic. Corrosive. May cause eye, skin, and respiratory tract irritation.
- 0.7M Phosphoric Acid: Toxic. Corrosive.
- 2M Sodium Hydroxide: Toxic. Corrosive. May cause eye, skin, and respiratory tract irritation.

Care should be taken when working with these reagents. Avoid inhalation and contact with skin, eyes, and clothing. Goggles, gloves, and lab coats are required at all times.

Part I— Determining the Calorimeter Constant

Set up the LabQuest© interface:

1. Connect temperature probes to CH1 and CH2 of LabQuest©.

2. Connect the USB cable to the computer and to LabQuest©.

3. Start Logger Pro© program. If your hardware has successfully connected, you will see the LabQuest© icon and "Temp1: *.**," "Temp2: *.**" right below the toolbar; there will also be a "Temperature 1 Temperature 2 vs Time" graph appear on the graph window.

4. Click the **Data Collection** button, change the **Length** of collection time from the default value of 180 seconds to 1250 seconds in **collection** Tile. Note: Simply changing the axis length will not change the length of Data Collection time.

5. Select **Column Options** by pulling down the **Data** menu, click temperature 1.

6. Select the **Column definition** Tile and input the name of the column as Hot Water. Press **Done** when ready.

7. Select **Column Options** by pulling down the **Data** menu, click temperature 2 and in the **Column definition** Tile, input the name of column as Cold Water. Press **Done** when ready.

Warning: the volume of water here is very important; measure the volume as precisely as possible by using a 50 mL graduated cylinder.

8. Add approximately 75 mL of deionized water to a 250 mL beaker. Using a hot plate, heat the water to about 80°C. Use a glass thermometer to measure the temperature of the hot water as it is heating on the hot plate. Do not rest the thermometer bulb on the bottom of the beaker, measure the temperature in the middle of the solution.

9. Place the calorimeter (2 nested polystyrene cups) in a 400 mL beaker to stabilize it. Carefully measure 50 mL of cold water using a 50 mL graduated cylinder and place it in the calorimeter. Cover the calorimeter with the cardboard cover and insert the CH2 probe in the cold water.

10. Place the empty polystyrene cup in another 400 mL beaker to stabilize it. When the hot water sample has reached the required temperature, carefully remove the hot water from the hot plate. Measure 50 mL of the hot water using the 50 mL graduated cylinder. Use a paper towel around the hot beaker to assist in pouring. Transfer the hot water to the empty cup. Cover with the cardboard cover and insert the CH1 probe into the hot water.

11. Now you are ready to begin measurement. Click the **Collect** button. After 2 minutes (120 seconds), rapidly pour the hot water from the hot water cup into the cold water in the calorimeter while stirring using the CH2 probe. Be sure that all the water has been transferred. Allow the CH1 probe to read air temperature while completing the experiment. Run an additional 3 minutes after mixing while recording the CH2 temperature (mixture temperature). **Stop** the run, **Autoscale** and **Save** the data using the appropriate file naming format.

12. To get the best graph, you have to modify this data file. In the Hot water column, select all the data points from the point of mixing the warm water to the end of the column and select **strike through data** from the **Edit** menu. Now you will see on the graph only the hot water data points collected before mixing the cold water.

13. Select the graph and choose **Graph Options** by pulling down the **Options** menu; in the **graph options** tile, input the title "Determining the Calorimeter Constant"; in **Axes options** tile, mark both **Hot Water** and **Cold Water** as Y Axis. Click **Done** when ready.

14. In the graph, select the points in the Hot water curve just **before** mixing and click the **Linear Fit** button. Select **Hot water** in the dialog box. Minimizing the box for this linear fit by clicking the (-)**box** and put it in a proper location.

15. In the graph, select the points in the Cold water curve just *before* mixing, click the **Linear Fit** button, select **Cold Water** in the dialog box. Minimize the box for this linear fit and put it in a proper place.

16. In the graph select the points in the Cold water curve *after* mixing, click the **Linear Fit** button and select **Cold Water** in the dialog box. Minimize the box for this linear fit and put it in a proper place.

17. Choose the **Interpolate** command by pulling down the **Analysis** menu. When you place your mouse cursor in the graph, there will be three corresponding values and a vertical line that appears. Place the vertical line such that it represents the point of mixing on the time scale. Remove the cursor carefully from the graph by moving it along

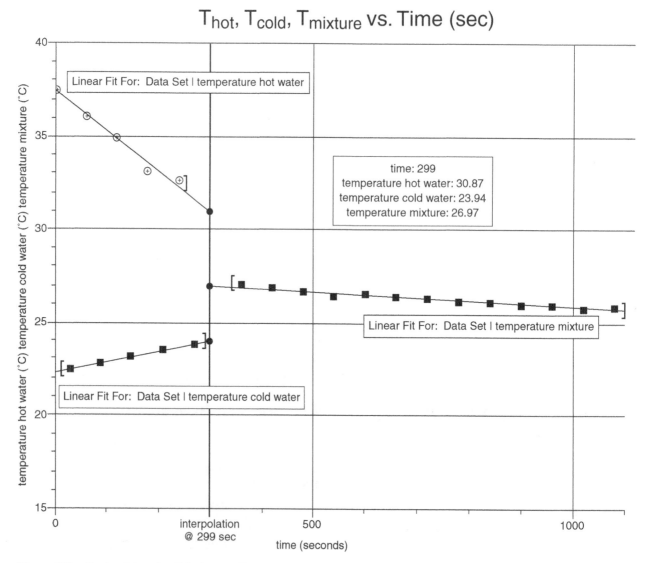

Figure 8.1   Determining the Calorimeter Constant

the vertical line up and off the page without moving the cursor horizontally. **Save** the data and **Print** out the graph showing the interpolation.

Do a second trial for the calorimeter constant. Do the calculation by using the values interpolated from the graph. Use Data Sheet 1 for your calculations and calculate a mean value from your two runs. A sample calculation is shown below. Your two values should be within 10% of each other. Don't forget to **Save** the data and **Print** the graphs for both trials.

SAMPLE CALCULATION 1

Two 50.0 g samples of water, one hot and the other cold, were mixed according to the instructions of the experiment. The temperature data is presented in Figure 8.1. Determine the calorimeter constant.

$q_{sys} = q_{hot} + q_{cold} + q_{cal} = 0$

$q_{hot} = mc\Delta T_{hot}$ where $\Delta T_{hot} = T_{final} - T_{initial} = 26.97°C - 30.87°C = -3.90°C$ $\left.\begin{array}{l}\\\\\end{array}\right\}$ Note

$q_{cold} = mc\Delta T_{cold}$ where $\Delta T_{cold} = T_{final} - T_{initial} = 26.97°C - 23.94°C = 3.03°C$ $\left.\begin{array}{l}\\\\\end{array}\right\}$ $|\Delta T_{hot}| > |\Delta T_{cold}|$

$q_{hot} = mc\Delta T_{hot} = (50.0\ g)(4.184\ J/g°C)(-3.90°C) = -815.88\ J$

$q_{cold} = mc\Delta T_{cold} = (50.0\ g)(4.184\ J/g°C)(3.03°C) = 633.876\ J$

$q_{cal} = C_{cal}\Delta T_{cold} = -(q_{hot} + q_{cold}) = -(-815.88\ J + 633.876\ J) = 182.004\ J$

$C_{cal} = q_{cal}/\Delta T_{cold} = 182.004\ J/3.03°C = 60.06733\ J/°C = 60.1\ J/°C$

Part II—Determine the Specific Heat and Molar Heat Capacity of Copper

1. Open up a new document of your Logger Pro$^©$ software for this part of the experiment and disconnect the CH2 probe from your LabQuest$^©$.
2. Click the **Data Collection** button, change the **Length** of collection time from the default value of 180 seconds to 1250 seconds in **collection** Tile. Note: Simply changing the axis length will not change the length of Data Collection time.
3. Select **Column Options** by pulling down the **Data** menu, click temperature 1 and in the **Column Definition** tile, input the name of column as Water Temperature. Press **Done** when ready.
4. Weigh the coil of copper wire on an analytical balance.
5. Use the hot plate to heat to boiling about 250 mL of water in a 400 mL beaker. Place the copper coil directly into the water. Bring the water to a boil and allow the copper to stay in the boiling water for at least 5 minutes.
6. Clean and dry the calorimeter. Weigh 75 g of room temperature deionized water in the calorimeter and record the weight to 0.01g. Stabilize the calorimeter in a 400 mL beaker and place the CH1 probe in the water.
7. Begin recording the temperature of the water in the calorimeter by clicking the **Collect** button. After approximately thirty seconds, use tongs, remove the coil from the hot water and briefly let the excess water drip off. Quickly and carefully, transfer the hot metal (assumed to be 100°C initially) into the calorimeter. Use the temperature probe to stir the water and record the temperature of the water with the heated copper until a stable temperature is reac hed, at least 2 minutes. Do not let the temperature probe touch the hot metal while stirring.
8. Select the graph and choose **Graph Options** by pulling down the **Options** menu; in the **graph options** tile, input the title "Water Temperature vs. Time"; in **Axes options** tile, mark **Cold Water** as Y Axis. Click **Done** when ready. **Autoscale** the graph.

9. Select the points in the Cold water curve just *before* adding the copper coil, click the **Linear Fit** button. Minimize the box for this linear fit and put it in a proper place.

10. In the graph select the points in the Cold water curve *after* mixing and click the **Linear Fit** button. Minimize the box for this linear fit and put it in a proper place.

11. Choose the **Interpolate** command by pulling down the **Analysis** menu. When you place your mouse cursor in the graph, there will be one corresponding value and a vertical line that appears. Place the vertical line such that it represents the point of addition of the hot copper on the time scale. Remove the cursor carefully from the graph by moving it along the vertical line up and off the page without moving the cursor horizontally. **Save** the data with a new file name, title and **Print** out the graph.

12. Use Data Sheet 2 to calculate the specific heat and molar heat capacity of copper. A sample calculation is shown on next page.

SAMPLE CALCULATION 2

A piece of a zinc that weighs 32.15 g is heated as described in the experiment to 100.00°C and immersed in 75.0 g of water in the calorimeter with C_{cal} = 60.1 J/°C. The initial temperature of the water was 24.10°C and its final temperature was 26.52°C. Determine the specific heat and molar heat capacity for the metal.

$$q_{sys} = q_{water} + q_{metal} + q_{cal} = 0$$
$$q_{cal} = -(q_{water} + q_{metal})$$
$$q_{cal} = C_{cal} \Delta T_{water}$$
$$\Delta T_{water} = T_{final} - T_{initial} = 26.52°C - 24.10°C = 2.42°C$$
$$\Delta T_{metal} = T_{final} - T_{initial} = 26.52°C - 100.00°C = -73.48°C$$
$$q_{cal} = C_{cal} \Delta T_{water} = (60.06733 \text{ J/°C}) \times (2.42°C) = 145.36294 \text{ J}$$
$$q_{water} = m_{water}c_{water} \Delta T_{water} = (75.0g) \times (4.184 \text{ J/g°C}) \times (2.42°C) = 759.396 \text{ J}$$
$$q_{metal} = -(q_{cal} + q_{water}) = -(145.36294 \text{ J} + 759.396 \text{ J}) = -904.75894 \text{ J}$$
$$q_{metal} = -904.75894 \text{ J} = m_{metal}c_{metal} \Delta T_{metal} = (32.15 \text{ g}) \times (c_{metal}) \times (-73.48°C)$$
$$c_{metal} = q_{metal}/m_{metal} \Delta T_{metal} = -904.75894 \text{ J}/((32.15g)(-73.48°C))$$
$$c_{metal} = 0.382986 \text{ J/g°C} = 0.383 \text{ J/g°C}$$
$$C_{metal} = (\text{molar heat capacity}) = c_{metal} MM_{metal}$$
$$= (0.382986 \text{ J/g°C}) (65.39 \text{ g/mol})$$
$$= 25.04345 \text{ J/mol°C}$$
$$= 25.0 \text{ J/mol°C}$$

Part III—Determining the Molar Enthalpy of Solution of a Salt

1. Clean and dry the calorimeter and open a new document of your Logger Pro© software.

2. Click the **Data Collection** button, change the **Length** of collection time from the default value of 180 seconds to 1250 seconds in **collection** Tile. Note: Simply changing the axis length will not change the length of Data Collection time.

3. Carefully measure about 75 g of room temperature deionized water in the calorimeter and record the mass to .01 g. Place the CH1 probe in the water and let the water temperature equilibrate in the calorimeter for 1 minute.

4. Weigh about 3 g of NH_4NO_3 to 0.001 g using weighing paper and record the exact weight on your data sheet.

5. Start recording the water temperature by clicking the **Collect** button.

6. After collecting the water temperature for about thirty seconds, rapidly and without losing any material, transfer the ammonium nitrate to the calorimeter. Mix with the probe until the salt is dissolved while recording the temperature for at least 3 minutes. Title the graph "Determining the Heat Solution of an Aqueous Ionic Salt." Perform the appropriate linear fits and interpolation to determine ΔT as you did in Part II—Determining the Specific Heat of Copper. **Save** the data with the appropriate file name and **Print** the graph with the interpolation shown.

7. Use Data Sheet 3 for the calculation of heat of solution. A sample calculation is shown below.

SAMPLE CALCULATION 3

A sample of salt weighing 3.00 g and with a molar mass of 100.0 g/mole is dissolved in **72.0 g** of water in the calorimeter with $C_{cal} = 60.1$ J/°C. Upon dissolution of the salt, the **solution** temperature drops 3.0°C. Determine the molar enthalpy of solution for the salt. (**Assume a specific heat for the solution to be equal to that for pure water, c = 4.184 J/gK**).

$$q_{system} = q_{solution} + q_{calorimeter} + q_{reaction} = 0$$

$$q_{cal} = C_{cal}\,\Delta T_{solution} = (60.06733 \text{ J/°C}) \times (-3.0°C) = -180.20199 \text{ J}$$

$$q_{solution} = m_{solution}c_{solution}\,\Delta T_{solution}$$

$$m_{solution} = 72.0 \text{ g} + 3.00 \text{ g} = 75.0 \text{ g} \quad c_{solution} = 4.184 \text{ J/g°C} \quad \Delta T_{solution} = -3.0°C$$

$$q_{solution} = (75.0g) \times (4.184J/g°C) \times (-3.0°C) = -941.4J$$

$$q_{reaction} = -(q_{solution} + q_{cal}) = -(-941.4J + -180.20199 \text{ J}) = 1121.60199 \text{ J}$$

$$\text{moles of salt} = (3.00 \text{ g}/(100.0 \text{ g/mole}) = 0.0300 \text{ mol}$$

$$\Delta H_{reaction} = (1121.60199 \text{ J}/0.0300 \text{ mol}) = 37386.733 \text{ J/mol} = 37.4 \times 10^3 \text{ J/mol}$$
$$= 37.4 \text{ kJ/mol}$$

Part IV—Determining the Molar Enthalpy of Neutralization.

1. Clean and dry the calorimeter and a 250mL beaker. Open a new document of your Logger Pro© software. Connect the CH2 probe once again to the LabQuest©.

2. Click the **Data Collection** button, change the **Length** of collection time from the default value of 180 seconds to 1250 seconds in **collection** Tile. Note: Simply changing the axis length will not change the length of Data Collection time.

3. Select **Column Options** by pulling down the **Data** menu; click **temperature 1** in **Column definition** Tile and input the name of the column as "Acid Temp." Press **Done** when ready.

4. Select **Column Options** by pulling down the **Data** menu, click **temperature 2** in **Column definition** Tile, input the name of column as "Base Temp." Press **Done** when ready.

5. You will be assigned an acid-base pair by your instructor: HCl-NaOH, H_2SO_4-NaOH, or H_3PO_4-NaOH. The concentration of the acids and the base can be determined from the labeled reagent bottles.

Warning: the volume of acid and base here is very important; measure the volume as precisely as possible using a volumetric pipet.

6. Stabilize your calorimeter in a 400 mL beaker. Using a 25 mL volumetric pipet, carefully measure *two* 25 mL portions of your assigned acid and add to your calorimeter. Insert the CH1 probe to your calorimeter.

7. Stabilize the single cup in a 400 ml beaker. Using a 25 mL volumetric pipet, carefully measure *two* 25 mL portions of your assigned base and add to your single cup. Insert the CH2 probe in single cup. Now you are ready for measurement.

8. Click the **Collect** button. After 1 minute, rapidly pour the base solution into the acid while stirring with the probe in the calorimeter. Be sure that all the base has been transferred. Place the cardboard cover on the calorimeter to minimize heat loss. Keep the CH1 probe in the calorimeter until you stop the experiment (run an additional 3 minutes after mixing). Allow the CH2 probe to stay in an empty beaker at air temperature. **Save** the data using a new file name.

9. As before, you must modify the file to get a good graph. In the Base column, select all the data points from the point that you mixed the solutions to the end of the column and select **strike through data** from the **Edit** menu. Now you will see just the points before mixing on the graph.

10. Select the graph, choose **Graph Options** by pulling down the **Options** menu, in **graph options** tile, input the title as "Determining the Molar Enthalpy of . . . (corresponding acid base pair name here)"; in **Axes options** tile and **mark** both **Acid** and **Base** as Y-Axis. Click **Done** when ready.

11. In the graph, select the points of the acid curve *before* mixing and click the **Linear Fit** button. Select **Acid** in the dialog box. Minimize the box for this linear fit and put it in a proper place.

12. In the graph, select the points in the base curve *before* mixing and click the **Linear Fit** button. Select **Base** in the dialog box. Minimize the box for this linear fit and put it in a proper place. The acid and base are both at room temperature and should both have the same initial temperature. However, if the base temperature is different, you can calculate a mean temperature for the initial temperature by averaging the acid and base initial temperature.

13. In the graph, select the points in the Acid curve *after* mixing, click the **Linear Fit** button, and select **Acid** in the dialog box. Minimize the box for this linear fit and put it in a proper place.

14. Choose the **Interpolate** command by pulling down the **Analysis** menu. Place your mouse cursor in the graph and there will be three corresponding values and the vertical line. Place the vertical line in such a way that it represents the point of mixing. Pull the cursor out of the graph by moving it up along the vertical line without moving the cursor horizontally. **Save** the data with a new file name and **Print** out the graph.

Use Data Sheet 4 for your calculations by using the ΔT values in the graph. A sample calculation is given below.

SAMPLE CALCULATION 4

The weak acid, 50.0 mL of 1.0 M hydrocyanic acid is neutralized by 50.0 mL of 1.05 M NaOH.

$$HCN_{(aq)} + NaOH_{(aq)} \rightarrow H_2O_{(l)} + NaCN_{(aq)}$$

The solution density is 1.06 g/mL and the specific heat is 3.77 J/g°C. Calculate the molar enthalpy of neutralization of this reaction. The temperature rise of the contents of the calorimeter was 1.50°C.

$$q_{system} = q_{solution} + q_{calorimeter} + q_{reaction} = 0$$

$$q_{cal} = C_{cal}\Delta T = (60.06733 \text{ J/°C}) \times (1.5°C) = 90.100995 \text{ J}$$

$$q_{solution} = m_{solution}c_{solution}\Delta T_{solution} = (1.06 \text{ g/mL})(100.0 \text{ mL}) \times (3.77 \text{ J/g°C})$$
$$\times (1.5°C) = 599.43 \text{ J}$$

$$q_{rxn} = -(q_{solution} + q_{cal}) = -(90.100995 \text{ J} + 599.43 \text{ J}) = -689.530995 \text{ J}$$

moles of acid = 0.0500 mol (This is the limiting reagent)

$$\Delta H_{reaction} = (-689.530995 \text{ J})/(0.0500 \text{ mol}) = -13,790.6199 \text{ J/mol}$$
$$= -13.8 \times 10^3 \text{ J/mole} = -13.8 \text{ kJ/mol}$$

TABLE 8.1 Heat Capacities and Densities for Reaction Mixtures

Solution	Concentration, M	Specific heat, J g^{-1} K^{-1}	Density, g mL^{-1}
Sodium chloride	1.00	3.89	1.04
Sodium hydrogen sulfate	1.00	3.80	1.09
Sodium sulfate	1.00	3.76	1.12
Sodium hydrogen phosphate	1.00	3.80	1.07
Sodium dihydrogen phosphate	1.00	3.80	1.05
Sodium phosphate	1.00	3.80	1.11
Water	–	4.184	1.00

DATA SHEET I

PART I—DETERMINING THE CALORIMETER CONSTANT

- Show a sample calculation for each type of calculated value.

	1st	*2nd*
$T_{initial\ hot}$	_____	_____
$T_{initial\ cold}$	_____	_____
$T_{final,\ mixture}$	_____	_____
ΔT_{hot}	_____	_____
ΔT_{cold}	_____	_____
volume hot water	_____	_____
volume cold water	_____	_____
q_{hot}	_____	_____
q_{cold}	_____	_____
$q_{calorimeter}$	_____	_____
C_{cal}	_____	_____
Average C_{cal}	_____	

DATA SHEET II

PART II—DETERMINING THE SPECIFIC HEAT AND MOLAR HEAT CAPACITY OF COPPER

- Show a sample calculation for each type of calculated value.

Calorimeter Constant: _____

	1st	*2nd*
$T_{initial, water}$	_____	_____
$T_{initial, metal}$	_____	_____
T_{final}	_____	_____
ΔT_{metal}	_____	_____
ΔT_{water}	_____	_____
mass of water	_____	_____
mass of metal	_____	_____
q_{cal}	_____	_____
q_{water}	_____	_____
q_{metal}	_____	_____
c_{metal}	_____	_____
molar heat capacity	_____	_____
Average molar heat capacity	_____	

DATA SHEET III

PART III—DETERMINING THE MOLAR ENTHALPY OF SOLUTION OF A SALT

- Show a sample calculation for each type of calculated value.

Calorimeter Constant: _____

	1st	*2nd*
$T_{initial, water}$	_____	_____
T_{final}	_____	_____
$\Delta T_{solution}$	_____	_____
mass of salt	_____	_____
moles of salt	_____	_____
mass of water	_____	_____
q_{cal}	_____	_____
$q_{solution}$	_____	_____
$q_{reaction}$	_____	_____
$\Delta H_{reaction}$	_____	_____
Average $\Delta H_{reaction}$	_____	

DATA SHEET IV

PART IV—DETERMINING THE MOLAR ENTHALPY OF NEUTRALIZATION

- Show a sample calculation for each type of calculated value.

Calorimeter Constant: _____

	1st	*2nd*
Acid name & concentration	_____	_____
Base name & concentration	_____	_____
$T_{initial, acid}$	_____	_____
$T_{initial, base}$	_____	_____
$T_{initial, average}$	_____	_____
T_{final}	_____	_____
$\Delta T_{solution}$	_____	_____
volume of acid	_____	_____
molarity of stock acid	_____	_____
moles of acid	_____	_____
volume of base	_____	_____
molarity of stock base	_____	_____
moles of base	_____	_____
q_{cal}	_____	_____
$q_{solution}$	_____	_____
$q_{reaction}$	_____	_____
$\Delta H_{reaction}$	_____	_____
Average $\Delta H_{reaction}$	_____	

Post-Laboratory Questions

---

1. Find a) the limiting reagent, b) the moles of reaction taking place, and c) the heat evolved in the reaction when 200mL of 0.02M H_2SO_4 reacts with 150mL of 0.05M NaOH according to the reaction:

   $$2NaOH(aq) + H_2SO_4(aq) \rightarrow Na_2SO_4(aq) + 2H_2O(l)$$

   $\Delta H°_{rxn} = -57.45$ kJ/mol

2. A 732 g sample of water was cooled from 60.0°C to 25.3°C. How much heat was lost? Would this process be considered endothermic or exothermic if the water is the system?

3. a. Discuss the ramifications of using a metal cup to run the experiments rather than the polystyrene calorimeter.

b. Would you expect the $\Delta H_{reaction}$ to be higher, lower, or the same in the calorimeter?

4. Discuss the importance of H (enthalpy) being a state function to this experiment.

BEFORE YOU COME TO LAB YOU MUST COMPLETE A PRELAB ASSIGNMENT:

Experiment 8: Chemistry and Thermodynamics Online PRELAB Quiz:

- The Chemistry and Thermodynamics Online PRELAB Quiz is composed of multiple choice questions. The PRELAB score accounts for 40 points of your total lab score.
- The PRELAB quiz is timed, and it must be submitted before **11:59pm the night before your experiment.**
- You may only submit the PRELAB quiz once.
- In order to prepare for your PRELAB quiz, it is recommended that you study the background information, calculations, and lab procedure for the experiment in your lab manual. You may be asked to perform calculations; the correct answer will need to be reported to the proper number of significant figures and with the appropriate units.
- You may be asked to prepare and print out a graph that you will turn into your instructors when you come to lab.

EXPERIMENT

9

Vitamin C Analysis—Redox Titration

BACKGROUND INFORMATION

History

Vitamin C is essential for our good health and our bodies cannot manufacture it. Most animals can make vitamin C from glucose, which is structurally very similar, but humans cannot.

Vitamin C is also known as "ascorbic acid" derived from the word "antiscorbutic," the term used in the 18th and 19th centuries as a generic term for substances know to prevent scurvy, prior to any full understanding of why this was true. Scurvy is caused by the serious deficiency of vitamin C in one's diet and results in the formation of liver spots on the skin, spongy gums, and bleeding from mucous membranes. The disease advances to open wounds, loss of teeth and eventually death.

The first scientific basis for the cause of scurvy was discovered by ship's surgeon, James Lind of the British Royal Navy. Lind, while at sea in May 1747, ran a controlled experiment with his sailors providing 2 oranges and 1 lemon per day to selected men. His results conclusively showed that citrus fruits prevented scurvy. Lind published his study in 1753 in his *Treatise on the Scurvy.* It wasn't until 1795 that the British Navy adopted lemons and limes as a supplement for their sailor's diet for the prevention of scurvy. The citrus fruit contained an anti-scorbutic factor that was thought to prevent scurvy.

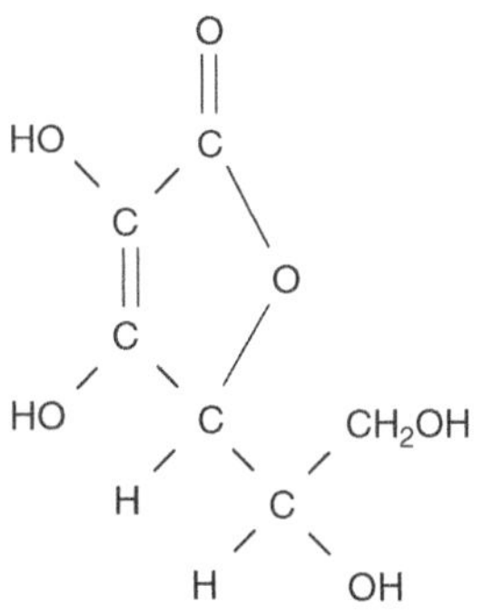

ascorbic acid

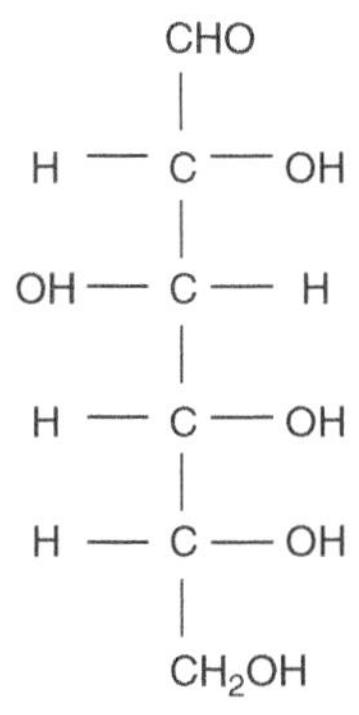

glucose

Figure 9.1 Ascorbic acid and glucose

In 1912, the biochemist Casimir Funk developed the concept of vitamins to refer to the non-mineral nutrients essential to health. Still not isolated, the anti-scorbutic factor was named "ascorbic acid" by Charles King of the University of Pittsburgh. Szent-Gyorgyi was also studying ascorbic acid isolated from lemon juice and thought it to be the anti-scorbutic factor. King and Szent-Gyorgyi simultaneously proved this was ascorbic acid. By 1934 Hoffman-La Roche, the pharmaceutical giant, bought the patent for manufacture of vitamin C and went into mass production under the brand name *Redoxon*. Ultimately, Szent-Gyorgyi received the 1937 Nobel Prize in Medicine with special mention of his work understanding vitamin C.

Linus Pauling, the great chemist and humanitarian who won 2 Nobel prizes (1954 Prize in Chemistry and 1962 Nobel Peace Prize), studied vitamin C and thought that mega doses could be used the treat the common cold as well as cancer. Research on vitamin C continues to this day. While many groups still promote large doses, it is generally accepted that the RDA (recommended daily allowance) is 60–95 mg per day (U.S. National Academy of Sciences). Vitamin C is considered to have the most beneficial effect of all nutrients (dietary supplement) on mortality and health in general, especially the health of the elderly.

Chemistry and Biology of Vitamin C

The process of chemical **oxidation** results in the loss of electrons while **reduction** results in the gain of electrons. In any **oxidation-reduction (redox) reaction**, the **reducing agent** is being oxidized while the **oxidizing agent** is being reduced. Transferred electrons in any redox reaction have to be balanced the same as atoms on each side of the equation.

Ascorbic acid (AA) is a **weak acid** and is also a **reducing agent**. We know that as a weak acid, it does not ionize completely in water, and so the H^+ ion concentration is relatively low as is the ascorbate ion.

Excess free radicals present in our bodies are reactive oxygen species that can create a condition called oxidative stress. This condition can result in cardiovascular disease, hypertension, chronic inflammatory disease, and diabetes. The ascorbate ion acts as reducing agent, or **antioxidant**, to reverse oxidation and to remove potentially harmful oxidizing agents from the body.

Analysis of Ascorbic Acid

We will use the oxidizing agent 2,6-dichloroindophenol (DCP) in the analysis of AA. DCP is chosen for this analysis because it conveniently changes color when reduced to

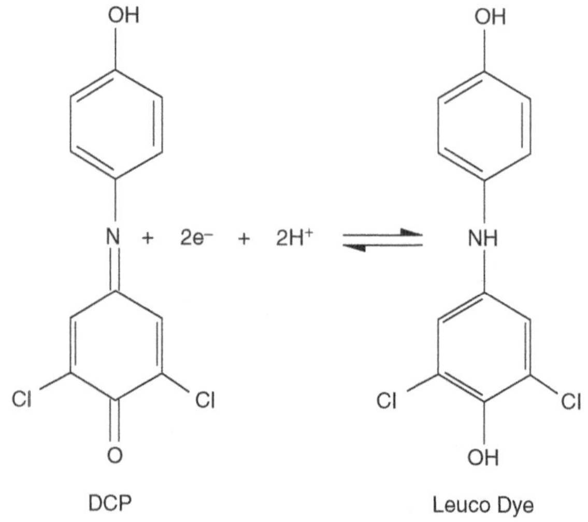

Figure 9.2   Reduction of DCP to Leuco Dye

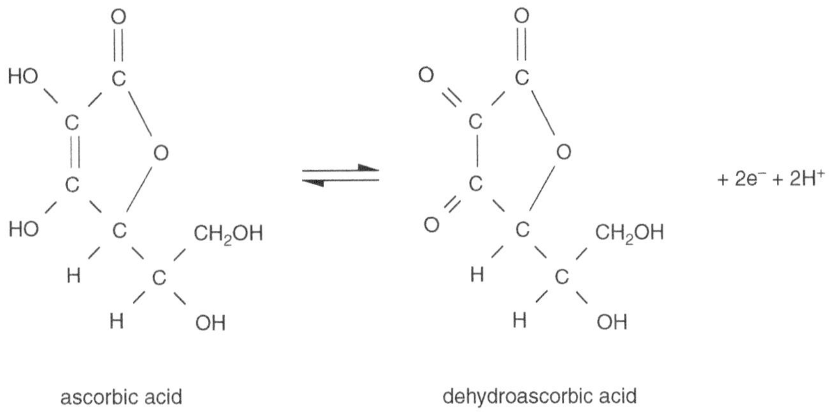

Figure 9.3 Oxidation of ascorbic acid to dehydroascorbic acid

its reaction product leuco dye. We will analyze for AA in orange and grapefruit juices and in a vitamin C supplement tablet.

This titration is different from other titrations we've done in lab where we monitored the pH of the solution to determine the end point. In this titration, the pH will not change since this is an oxidation/reduction reaction or a redox titration. We need some other means of measuring the end point. When titrating a solution containing AA, as long as some AA remains in solution, the blue DCP is reduced to colorless leuco dye. The reduction of DCP to leuco dye is shown in Figure 9.2 The oxidation of AA to dehydroascorbic acid is shown in Figure 9.3. Once the vitamin C is completely oxidized, the next bit of DCP imparts a pink color to the solution (that is sustained for 30 seconds) and this is our end point. While the DCP is initially blue in color, it turns pink in an acidic medium.

$C_6H_8O_6$ (*aq*, colorless) + $C_{12}H_7O_2NCl_2$ (*aq*, blue) →
vitamin C   DCP

$C_6H_6O_6$ (*aq*, colorless) + $C_{12}H_9O_2NCl_2$ (*aq*, colorless)
dehydroascorbic acid   leuco dye

To avoid any potential chemical interference, we add metaphosphoric acid $(HPO_3)_n$ and a pH 3 buffer to the reaction mixture to achieve three goals:

1. Metaphosphoric acid is used to denature and precipitate proteins from food or juice samples. Any proteins present would react with DCP and appear to be vitamin C.

2. We will lower the pH to 3 so that side reactions of DCP with any species other than vitamin C are prevented (such as phenols and sulfhydryl compounds which react with DCP @ pH>4).

3. Also lowering the pH to 3 will inhibit the ionization and decomposition of vitamin C.

Standardizing DCP

Many important chemical reagents are extremely reactive. As a result, reactive reagents must be standardized before using to have an accurate measure of its concentration because the concentration of a reactive reagent will decrease over time as the reagent degrades. The important reagent, NaOH(aq) is one such chemical. DCP also falls into this category of very reactive chemicals that must be standardized just prior to use. To standardize the DCP, we prepare a solution of known concentration of "reagent grade AA" (100% purity assumed), and then run the titration to the end point and calculate the concentration of the DCP by applying the known rules of stoichiometry. A sample calculation is given below.

Sample Calculation 1:

A student weighed 45.6 mg of reagent grade AA and dissolved it in 50.00 mL of deionized water. The student then extracted 3–5.00 mL samples using a 5 mL volumetric pipet and placed each in a 125 mL Erlenmeyer flask. The student then added approximately 10 mL of deionized water and 5 mL of pH3 buffer to each flask and proceeded to titrate the samples with the DCP reagent. The respective titrations required 28.53, 28.86 and 29.08 mL of DCP. Calculate the mean concentration of the DCP.

$$\text{moles of AA weighed} = \frac{4.56 \times 10^{-2}\,g}{176.124\,\frac{g}{mol}} = 2.589085 \times 10^{-4}\,mole$$

$$\text{moles of AA titrated} = \left(2.589085 \times 10^{-4}\,moles\right)\left(\frac{5.00 \times 10^{-3}\,L}{5.000 \times 10^{-2}\,L}\right)$$

$$= 2.589085 \times 10^{-5}\,moles$$

$$\text{moles AA titrated} = \text{moles DCP} = M_{DCP}V_{DCP}$$

$$M_{DCP} = \frac{2.589085 \times 10^{-5}\,moles}{2.853 \times 10^{-2}\,L} = 9.0749562 \times 10^{-4}\,M$$

$$M_{DCP} = 9.0749562 \times 10^{-4}\,M\ (trial1)$$

$$M_{DCP} = 8.9711885 \times 10^{-4}\,M\ (trial2)$$

$$M_{DCP} = 8.9033184 \times 10^{-4}\,M\ (trial3)$$

$$\text{Mean }M_{DCP} = \frac{(9.0749562 + 8.9711885 + 8.9033184) \times 10^{-4}\,M}{3}$$

$$= 8.9831544 \times 10^{-4}\,M = 8.98 \times 10^{-4}\,M$$

Determining the AA Content of a Juice or Vitamin C Supplement

Once the molarity of your DCP has been determined, it can be used to determine the AA content of an unknown such as orange juice, grapefruit juice or vitamin C supplement. The molar amounts of DCP and AA are always the same as a result of the stoichiometry. Therefore, when the moles of DCP are determined, if we multiply by the molar mass of AA, 176.124 g/mole, we calculate the mass in grams of AA in the titrated sample. Compare this amount to the recommended daily allowance (RDA) of vitamin C that is recommended for humans by the National Academy of Sciences and the United States Department of Agriculture. That amount is 60.0 mg per day for adults over 15 years of age. Pregnant women and smokers require more than this nominal amount.

Sample Calculation 2:

A student measured a 10.00 mL sample of filtered juice using a 10 mL volumetric pipet and placed it in a 250 mL Erlenmeyer flask that already contained 20 mL of metaphosphoric acid and 10 mL of pH3 buffer. The student then proceeded to titrate the sample with the DCP reagent previously standardized at $8.9831544 \times 10^{-4}\,M$. The titration required 16.63 mL of DCP. What is the %RDA of Vitamin C in 6 fl. oz of juice? (1.00 fl. oz = 29.5735 mL)

$$\text{moles of DCP} = 8.9831544 \times 10^{-4} M \times 1.663 \times 10^{-2} L$$

$$= 1.493898577 \times 10^{-5} moles = moles \ of \ AA \ titrated$$

$$\text{mass of AA titrated} = \left(1.493898577 \times 10^{-5} moles \times 176.124 \frac{g}{mol} \right)$$

$$= 2.631113929 \times 10^{-3} grams \ of \ AA \ in \ 10 \, mL \ sample$$

$$\frac{2.631113929 \times 10^{-3} grams}{10 \, mL} = 2.631113929 \times 10^{-4} \frac{gAA}{mL}$$

$$\left(2.631113929 \times 10^{-4} \frac{gAA}{mL} \right) \times \left(\frac{29.5735 \, mL}{1.00 \ fl.oz} \right) \times 6 \ fl.oz.$$

$$= 4.66867487 \times 10^{-2} gAA \ in \ 6 \ fl.oz.$$

$$= 46.6867487 \ mg \ AA \ in \ 6 \ fl.oz.$$

$$\frac{46.6867487 \ mg \ AA}{60.0 \ mg \ AA} \times 100\% = 77.81124779\%$$

$$= 77.8\% \ RDA \ of \ Vitamin \ C \ in \ 6 \ fl.oz.of \ juice$$

Sample Calculation 3:

A student finely crushed a vitamin C tablet weighing 1.097 g and quatitatively transferred the powder with 15 mL of 3% metaphosphoric acid to a 100 mL volumetric flask. The solution was diluted to 100.00 mL with deionized water. A 5.00 mL sample of this solution was transferred to a 125 mL Erlenmeyer flask with a 5 mL volumetric pipet. To this Erlenmeyer flask the student added 5 mL of pH 3 buffer and an additional 25 mL of deionized water and 10 mL of 3% metaphosphoric acid. The student then proceeded to titrate the mixture in the Erlenmeyer flask with DCP previously standardized at $8.9831544 \times 10^{-4} M$. The titration required 30.60 mL of titrant. What is the mass (in mg) of Ascorbic Acid in the original tablet?

$$\text{moles of DCP} = 8.9831544 \times 10^{-4} M \times 3.060 \times 10^{-2} \ L$$

$$= 2.748845246 \times 10^{-5} moles = moles \ of \ AA$$

$$\text{mass of AA titrated} = \left(2.748845246 \times 10^{-5} moles \times 176.124 \frac{g}{mol} \right)$$

$$= 4.8413762 \times 10^{-3} grams \ of \ AA \ in \ 5.00 \, mL \ sample$$

$$\frac{4.8413762 \times 10^{-3} grams}{5.00 \, mL} \times 100.00 \, mL = 9.6827524 \times 10^{-2} \frac{gAA}{tablet}$$

$$= 9.68 \times 10^{-2} \frac{gAA}{tablet} = 96.8 \frac{mgAA}{tablet}$$

PURPOSE

1. Standardize DCP—report average concentration and standard deviation
2. Juice sample—compare vitamin C content to the reported RDA
3. Vitamin Supplement—compare vitamin C content to the reported RDA

PROCEDURE

Chemical Hazards:

- 3% Metaphosphoric Acid: Toxic and corrosive.
- pH 3 Buffer: May cause eye, skin, and respiratory tract irritation.
- Ascorbic Acid: May cause eye, skin, and respiratory tract irritation.
- 2,6-Dichloroindophenol: May cause eye, skin, and respiratory tract irritation.

Care should be taken when working with these reagents. Avoid inhalation and contact with skin, eyes, and clothing. Goggles, gloves, and lab coats are required at all times.

Part I—Standardizing the DCP Solution

For this part of the lab, you will need the following glassware and pieces of equipment: 1 buret, 1 50-mL volumetric flask, 3 125-mL Erlenmeyer flasks, a 50-mL graduated cylinder, an automatic pipet, a magnetic stirrer, and a magnetic stirring bar. Review Appendix III for proper preparation and usage of glassware—pay particular attention to the section on volumetric pipets, automatic pipets, and volumetric flasks. REMEMBER, the automatic pipet is a very delicate piece of equipment, so please review Appendix III before use.

Some things to keep in mind as you use the automatic pipet:

- NEVER lay the pipet on its side, always return the pipet to a pipet stand when not in use to avoid damage to the pipet.
- Practice using the pipet before performing the experiment; ask your instructor if you have any questions.
- Do not set volumes outside the pipet's volume range.
- REFER to Appendix III for instructions on using the automatic pipet.

1. Using an analytical balance, carefully weigh one sample of reagent grade ascorbic acid, between 40–60 mg. Record the exact mass as required on Data Sheet I.
2. Transfer the sample to a 50 mL volumetric flask and fill the flask with enough deionized water to make the volume 50.00 mL. Mix this solution thoroughly by inverting the flask five times. Pour the solution into a clean, labeled beaker.
3. Rinse the cleaned buret with 3–5 mL of DCP solution and discard. Fill the buret with DCP solution past the 0.0 mL mark. Drain some DCP until the level is between 0 and 5 mL, and no air bubbles remain in the tip. Record this initial level (to the nearest 0.01 mL) on Data Sheet I.
4. After properly preparing and cleaning the equipment, using an automatic pipet, carefully transfer three 5.00 mL portions of the ascorbic acid solution prepared above to three labeled Erlenmeyer flasks. To each Erlenmeyer add an additional 20 mL of deionized water using a graduated cylinder and 10 mL of pH 3 buffer using an automatic pipet in the hood.
5. You can now proceed with the titration of the three samples. Place the first of the three Erlenmeyer flasks on a magnetic stirrer with a piece of blank white paper under the flask and begin to titrate with the DCP solution. Continue *slowly* adding titrant until the pink color persists for longer than a few seconds. Slow down the flow of DCP and continue to titrate until the solution turns slightly pink and remains so for longer than thirty seconds. Record the DCP solution level from the buret on Data Sheet I.

6. Refill your buret with DCP and repeat the titration for the remaining two solutions. Be careful to titrate each of these to the same color as the first solution. Record the initial and final buret readings on Data Sheet I.

7. Finish the calculations on Data Sheet I and determine the concentration of the DCP solution to be used for the remainder of the lab. Dispose of the waste solutions in accordance with the instructions. Wash all glassware thoroughly for the next part of the experiment.

Part II—Analyzing Juices for Vitamin C Content

For this section of the lab, you will need a clean glass funnel and a piece of cotton. You will also need to have ready three 250 mL Erlenmeyer flasks, an automatic pipet and a buret for the DCP solution.

1. Place a small piece of cotton in the neck of a glass funnel. Place the funnel in a 50 mL graduated cylinder. In a clean beaker, obtain 40 mL of juice. Record the brand and type of juice on Data Sheet II. Pass this juice through the filtering funnel you have just constructed two times, changing the cotton in the funnel for the 2nd filtration.

2. Transfer 20 mL of metaphosphoric acid and 10 mL of pH 3 buffer to a clean 250 mL Erlenmeyer flask using the automatic pipets in the hood. With your automatic pipet, transfer 10.00 mL of clear juice to the Erlenmeyer.

3. Refill your buret with DCP solution and record the initial volume on Data Sheet II. Titrate the juice/acid mixture in the same manner as done in Part I of this experiment. Using a sheet of white paper for clarity, add DCP slowly until the pink color persists

$$\% \text{ Relative Error} = \left| \frac{(1\text{st value} - 2\text{nd value}) \times 100}{1\text{st value}} \right| \qquad \text{Eq. 9.1}$$

for 30 seconds. Record this final buret reading on Data Sheet II and determine the amount of DCP used in the titration. Perform a second trial for this experiment as done above. If the results of this trial result in the same vitamin C content within 10% relative error, proceed. Otherwise, perform a third trial.

Part III—Analyzing a Vitamin Supplement for Vitamin C Content

For this section of the lab you will require a mortar and pestle, an automatic pipet, 2 or 3 125 mL Erlenmeyer flasks, one each 50 mL and 100 mL volumetric flasks, and a buret for standardized DCP solution.

Note: This procedure requires multiple dilutions of the vitamin C tablet solution to obtain concentrations in the appropriate range.

1. Obtain one vitamin C tablet from your instructor and accurately weigh it with an analytical balance (do not omit any precision). Record the mass on Data Sheet III. Transfer the tablet to a 70-mm mortar.

2. Add 15 mL of 3% metaphosphoric acid solution to the mortar and grind the solid as finely as possible with a pestle. Transfer the contents of the mortar to a 100 mL volumetric flask. Rinse the mortar with 20 mL of deionized water and transfer the rinses to the volumetric flask. Rinse and transfer again. Fill the volumetric flask to 100 mL with deionized water. Mix the solution by inverting the flask several times and pour the solution into a clean, labeled beaker.

3. Transfer 5.00 mL of this mixture to a 125 mL Erlenmeyer flask with an automatic pipet. To this flask use appropriately sized graduated cylinders add 10 mL of 3% metaphosphoric acid, 5 mL pH 3 buffer, and 25 mL of deionized water. Titrate this sample with the standardized DCP solution as you did in Part II of this experiment. Record the initial and final DCP volumes on Data Sheet III.

4. Repeat this procedure by transferring a 2nd 5.00 mL sample of the solution as in step 3 and duplicate the titration procedure. If the results of these two titrations result in the same vitamin C contents within 10%, proceed. Otherwise, perform a third trial of this experiment as needed. Clean and discard all the solutions as indicated by your laboratory instructor.

DATA SHEET I

PART I—STANDARDIZING THE DCP SOLUTIONS

- Show a sample calculation for each type of calculated value.
- To maintain accuracy, use the same analytical balance throughout this experiment.
- Rinse the buret with a small amount of DCP solution after cleaning with deionized water.
- Check again that the DCP solutions are room temperature before proceeding. If they are not, consult your laboratory instructor.

Mass of weighing boat   _____

Mass of weighing boat and ascorbic acid   _____

Mass of ascorbic acid   _____

	Trial 1	*Trial 2*	*Trial 3*
Initial buret reading	_____	_____	_____
Final buret reading	_____	_____	_____
Volume DCP added	_____	_____	_____
Moles of ascorbic acid titrated	_____	_____	_____
Concentration of DCP:	_____	_____	_____

Average DCP Solution Concentration, *M:*   _____

Standard Deviation: _____

DATA SHEET II

PART II—TITRATING JUICE SAMPLES WITH STANDARDIZED DCP

- Show a sample calculation for each type of calculated value.
- To maintain accuracy, use the same analytical balance throughout this experiment.
- Make sure that the DCP you are using in this section is from the same batch that you standardized in Part I.
- 1.000 fl. oz = 29.5735 mL

Juice brand being assayed: _____

DCP concentration (from Part I): _____

	Trial 1	*Trial 2*	*Trial 3*
Volume of juice	_____	_____	_____
Initial buret reading	_____	_____	_____
Final buret reading	_____	_____	_____
Volume DCP required	_____	_____	_____
Number of moles of DCP required for titration	_____	_____	_____
Mass of ascorbic acid in the juice sample	_____	_____	_____
Mass of ascorbic acid per milliliter of juice	_____	_____	_____
Average mass of ascorbic acid per milliliter of juice			_____
Mass of ascorbic acid in a 6-fl. oz serving of titrated juice			_____
Percent RDA of ascorbic acid in a 6-fl. oz serving of juice			_____

DATA SHEET III

PART III—ANALYZING VITAMIN C TABLET WITH STANDARDIZED DCP

- Show a sample calculation for each type of calculated value.
- To maintain accuracy, use the same analytical balance throughout this experiment.
- Make sure that the DCP you are using in this section is from the same batch that you standardized in Part I.

Product being assayed: _____

DCP concentration (from Part I): _____

	Trial 1	*Trial 2*	*Trial 3*
Mass of weighing boat	_____	_____	_____
Mass of weighing boat and the solid sample	_____	_____	_____
Mass of the solid sample	_____	_____	_____
Initial buret reading	_____	_____	_____
Final buret reading	_____	_____	_____
Volume DCP required	_____	_____	_____
Number of moles of DCP required for titration	_____	_____	_____
Mass of ascorbic acid titrated	_____	_____	_____
Mass of ascorbic acid per tablet	_____	_____	_____
Average amount of ascorbic acid per tablet			_____

Post-Laboratory Questions

1. In the background materials it was discussed that fresh fruits and vegetables contain a large amount of vitamin C.
   Describe the process by which a sample of Indian gooseberry could be evaluated for its vitamin C content.

2. Could the same procedure you outlined for the gooseberry sample be used to assay the vitamin C content of tomato juice? Explain.

3. How would the following experimental errors change the calculation of the number of mg of ascorbic acid in fresh orange juice?
   a. Students neglected to filter the juice.

   b. The DCP was standardized properly but it was done the previous day.

c. The student neglected to add the pH 3 buffer.

d. The student neglected to add the metaphosphoric acid.

4. Another example of a redox titration is the reaction below,

$$MnO_4^-(aq) + 5Fe^{2+}(aq) + 8H^+(aq) \rightarrow Mn^{2+}(aq) + 5Fe^{3+}(aq) + 4H_2O(l)$$

          (purple)   (colorless)

This titration can be used to estimate the amount of iron in iron supplement. If it takes 29.35 mL of 0.125M MnO_4^- solution to titrate 35 mL of Fe^{2+} solution, what is the molar concentration of the Fe^{2+} solution?

BEFORE YOU COME TO LAB YOU MUST COMPLETE A PRELAB ASSIGNMENT:

Experiment 9: Vitamin C Analysis- Redox Titration Online PRELAB Quiz:

- The Vitamin C Analysis Online PRELAB Quiz is composed of multiple choice questions.
- The PRELAB score accounts for 40 points of your total lab score.
- The PRELAB quiz is timed, and it must be submitted before **11:59pm the night before your experiment.**
- You may only submit the PRELAB quiz once.
- In order to prepare for your PRELAB quiz, it is recommended that you study the background information, calculations, and lab procedure for the experiment in your lab manual. You may be asked to perform calculations; the correct answer will need to be reported to the proper number of significant figures and with the appropriate units.
- You may be asked to prepare and print out a graph that you will turn into your instructors when you come to lab.

10

Transition Metal Complexes and Beer's Law

BACKGROUND INFORMATION

Transition Metal Complexes

Transition metals ions are Lewis acids which form stable acid-base reaction products known as complexes or **coordination complexes.** A **Lewis acid** is any species which accepts an electron pair while a Lewis base is any species that donates an electron pair. In complex formation, the bases are ions, or polar neutral molecules (such as H_2O, NH_3, CN^-, and Cl^-) and are called **ligands.**

The naming of complexes is different from the "Stock" system we have used for naming inorganic compounds. In naming complexes, we name the ligand first followed by the metal. For example, $Al(NH_3)_6^{3+}$ is hexaamminealuminum(III) ion and $Cu(H_2O)_6^{2+}$ is hexaaquacopper(II) ion. The ligand Cl^- is named chloro and CN^- is cyano in complex formation.

Coordination complexes have many important properties. They form brilliantly colored aqueous solutions which are a result of the electronic structure of transition metals. More specifically the colors of the solutions are due to the electron transitions involving the d electrons. The energies associated with these transitions are a function of the identity and number of ligands, the oxidation state of the metal, and the period to which the metal belongs. The combination of these effects determines the wavelength (λ) of the absorbed light. Solutions that absorb light in the visible region give rise to colored solutions. The perceived color of the solution has a complementary relationship with the color of the absorbed light. See Table 10.1 below.

Table 10.1 Relation between Wavelength, Color, and Complementary Color

Wavelength, nm	Color	Complementary Color
380–435	violet	yellow-green
435–490	green-blue	orange
490–500	blue-green	red
500–560	green	purple
560–580	yellow-green	violet
580–595	yellow	blue
595–610	orange	green-blue
610–750	red	blue-green

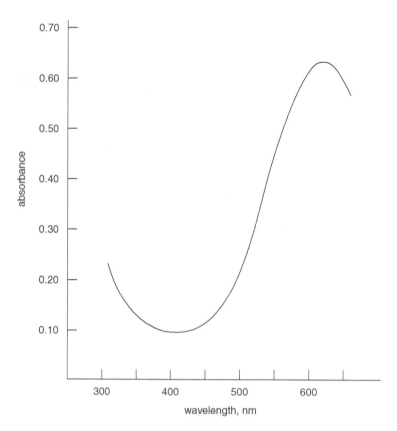

Figure 10.1   Absorbance vs. wavelength for tetraamminecopper(II) ion aqueous solution

In this experiment, we will study the complex ion $[Cu(NH_3)_4]^{2+}$ (tetraamminecopper(II) ion). This complex ion forms aqueous solutions that absorb light in the red/orange (visible) region. Solutions appear blue since blue light is not absorbed and passes through the solution. What we see is the light that is not absorbed. The absorbance "peaks" at a particular λ (wavelength). In the case of $[Cu(NH_3)_4]^{2+}$, the wavelength peaks at about 620 nm which corresponds to red/orange light and is called the analytical wavelength. See Figure 10.1 above.

Beer's Law (or Beer-Lambert's Law)

The higher the concentration of the complex ion, the greater the light absorption and the more intense is the blue color. We can determine the concentration of an unknown solution by comparing the color intensity to that of a standard solution of known concentration. Absorbance is also proportional to the **path length** or the distance the light travels through the sample. The greater the path length (the thicker the sample) the more complete is the light absorption. Finally, the absorbance is proportional to a species specific factor called the molar absorptivity, ϵ, which is also a function of the wavelength and is a measure of how strongly a specific species absorbs light at a given wavelength. Since we run our experiment at a fixed wavelength, the molar absorptivity is a constant for the experiment. The molar absorptivity is also called the extinction coefficient. Path length is usually fixed at 1.0 cm for convenience. See Figure 10.2.

Absorbance is proportional to:

- concentration, C (molarity)
- path length, b (cm)
- molar absorptivity, ϵ ($M^{-1}cm^{-1}$)

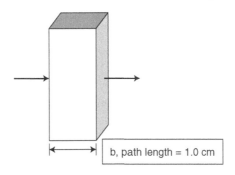

Figure 10.2   The path length

Beer's Law

$$A = \epsilon bC \qquad\qquad \text{Eq. 10.1}$$

A plot of A (absorbance) vs. C (molar concentration) will yield a straight line with a slope of ϵb which passes through the origin. Beer's Law does not necessarily apply to all solution concentrations and depending on the molar absorptivity of a particular species, the range for which the linear relationship holds can be determined experimentally. Trying to apply Beer's law outside that given range of concentrations will result in an unreliable result. Typically, solutions transmitting more than 90% of incident light or less than 10% of incident light will deviate from Beer's Law.

The LabQuest© Interface and Logger Pro© software

The LabQuest© Interface colorimeter emits light at four different wavelengths which can be matched to any experiment. Light passes through the solution and strikes a photo diode which produces an electrical voltage which is converted to a digital signal by the interface. Voltage is proportional to the light intensity. Voltage is *logarithmically* related to the absorbance.

$$A = -\log\frac{V}{V_0} = \epsilon bC$$

$$= \log V_0 - \log V$$

where:

$$V_0 = \text{voltage for a reference blank}$$

$$V = \text{voltage for the sample}$$

The reference or blank contains everything but the sample being studied (cuvet, solvent, etc.). The blank allows us to compensate for the extraneous absorption from the cuvet, solvent, etc., which is subtracted when we calibrate the instrument. Absorbance cannot be measured directly with the LabQuest© Interface, instead we measure % transmittance (%T), that is, how much light is not absorbed (how much light passes through the solution). Absorbance is simultaneously calculated and recorded in the data table.

$$A = -\log\frac{I}{I_0} \quad \text{where I is the intensity of light transmitted by the sample \& } I_0$$
is the intensity of light transmitted by the blank. $I/I_0 \times 100 = \%T$

$$= -\log\frac{\%T}{100}$$

$$= 2 - \log \%T$$

We can write: $A = 2.000 - \log(\%T) = \epsilon bC \qquad\qquad \text{Eq. 10.2}$

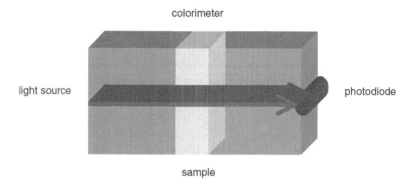

colorimeter

light source

photodiode

sample

Voltage is proportional
to the light intensity

Figure 10.3   Schematic of the LabQuest$^{©}$ colorimeter

A schematic of the LabQuest$^{©}$ colorimeter is shown in Figure 10.3. Monochromatic light passes through the sample and strikes a photodiode. The detector converts the light intensity to a logarithmically proportional voltage signal.

If we prepare several solutions with known concentration, then write Beer's Law $A = (\epsilon b) \cdot C$ and plot A vs. C, we get a straight line (Figure 10.4). We can now use this "standard" data to determine the concentration of an "unknown" solution. Simply measure the absorbance of the unknown solution and see what concentration corresponds from the Beer's Law plot. Since the slope of the line is ϵb, if we measure b, the path length, we can calculate the molar absorptivity (ϵ) for the species.

We will combine a 0.10M stock of $CuSO_4$(aq) (which contains $[Cu(H_2O)_6]^{2+}$ complex ion) with ammonia solution to form $[Cu(NH_3)_4]^{2+}$ complex ions. Precisely dilute with water to produce a set of 10 standards. You will measure %T and A for each standard.

Since you prepared the standards, the concentrations are known. You can then plot A vs. C. When using the Logger Pro$^{©}$ software, you will be prompted to enter the solution concentrations as you make the absorbance determinations.

Then determine ϵ, $\epsilon = f(\lambda, \text{species})$. Obtain an "unknown" solution, carefully dilute it to produce 3 solutions. Measure the %T and A for each solution. From the Beer's Law Plot, determine their concentration. Finally, calculate the unknown concentration of the original solution before dilution.

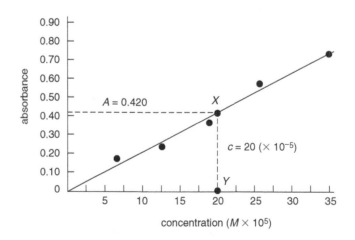

Figure 10.4   Standard Beer's Law plot

PURPOSE

The purpose of this experiment is to understand the concept and application of Beer's Law. It is very important to know the limitations of Beer's Law and its applicability in a real chemical system. In today's experiment, you will:

- Prepare a Beer's law plot over an applicable concentration range for the $[Cu(NH_3)_4]^{2+}$ system. (2 graphs)
- Calculate the molar absorptivity for this simple chemical system.
- Determine the concentration of an unknown solution using the Beer's Law plot.

INSTRUMENTATION AND EQUIPMENT

The instrumentation that you need in this lab will be:

- One LabQuest$^{©}$ interface.
- One colorimeter and one cuvet.
- one or two 25 mL volumetric flasks
- one 5 mL automatic pipet

PROCEDURE

Chemical Hazards:

- 2.5M Ammonia Solution: Causes eye, skin, and respiratory tract irritation. Toxic if inhaled, swallowed, or absorbed through the skin. Vapor harmful: toxic if inhaled. Work with ammonia solutions in the hood to avoid inhalation of vapors. Do not add ammonia to empty volumetric flasks.
- 0.1M Copper(II) Sulfate: Toxic. Causes eye, skin, and respiratory tract irritation.

Care should be taken when working with these reagents. Avoid inhalation and contact with skin, eyes, and clothing. Goggles, gloves, and lab coats are required at all times.

Preparing the Beer's Law Plot

Set up your LabQuest$^{©}$ interface:

1. connect colorimeter to CH1 of LabQuest$^{©}$. A green LED will show you that it is connected.
2. connect the USB cable the computer and to LabQuest$^{©}$.
3. Start Logger Pro$^{©}$ program. If your hardware has successfully connected, you will see the LabQuest$^{©}$ status "Transmittance: *.**," right below the toolbar.

4. Click **Open** button and open "Beer's Law " from the "<Chemistry with Vernier>" folder. Create a personal file by selecting **Save As** and naming the file as "Beer's Lab Locker#." Save the file to your folder.

Part I—Preparing Solutions and Calibration

1. Obtain approximately 45 mL of CuSO₄ solution (0.10M) in a 50mL beaker.
2. You will be using an automatic pipet. This piece of equipment is very delicate, so please review Appendix III before use.

   Some things to keep in mind as you use the automatic pipet:

   - NEVER lay the pipet on its side, always return the pipet to a pipet stand when not in use to avoid damage to the pipet.
   - Practice using the pipet before performing the experiment; ask your instructor if you have any questions.
   - Do not set volumes outside the pipet's volume range.
   - REFER to Appendix III for instructions on using the automatic pipet.

   Dispense 0.50 mL of CuSO₄ solution (0.10M) into the 25 mL volumetric flask , add approximately 10 mL of deionized water, go to the hood and add 2.50 mL of 2.5 M NH₃ solution. then fill up to the line with deionized water.

3. Mix the solution thoroughly and pour into a clean and dry labeled 15 mL test tube for later colorimetric measurement (reminder: you have to fill the test tube as much as possible to make sure that you have enough solution for two trials).
4. Repeat steps 2 & 3 using 2.50 mL of 2.5M ammonia solution with 1.00, 1.50, 2.00, 2.50, 3.00, 3.50, 4.00, 4.50, and 5.00 mL of copper(II) sulfate (0.10M) solution. Add the copper solution and 10 mL of deionized water to the 25mL volumetric flask before adding the ammonia solution. Do not add the ammonia solution to an empty flask.
5. Calculate all concentrations of solutions as molarity (moles per liter).
6. Prepare the blank solution with 2.50 mL of 2.5M ammonia solution plus water to 25.00 mL. Once the solution is prepared it can be transferred to a (labeled) test tube.

Calibration: Select a wavelength of 635 nm for the colorimeter to turn on the red LED inside the colorimeter (you can see it when you open the lid of the colorimeter).
Calibrate the colorimeter as follows:

1. Warning: the cuvet has a volume of approximately 4 mL. Two opposite sides of the cuvet are ribbed and are not intended to transmit the light from the LED. The two smooth surfaces are intended to transmit light. It is important to position the cuvet correctly in the chamber.
2. Place the cuvet containing the reference solution (blank) into the chamber of the colorimeter; press the **CAL** (auto-calibration) on the panel of the colorimeter until the red LED begins to flash, then release the CAL.
3. When the LED stops flashing, the calibration is done. It is only necessary to calibrate once per series of measurements, unless you exit the Logger Pro© program. Now you are ready to begin measurement.

Part II—Creating a Standard Plot

1. Click **Collect** button.

2. Carefully transfer about 3.5 mL of the first copper solution into the cuvet and replace the cuvet cap; rinse and dry the outside of cuvet with a Kimwipe and place the cuvet in the chamber of colorimeter and close the cover.

3. In the LabQuest© status ("Transmittance: *.* right below the toolbar, when these two values are stable (maybe with some very small fluctuation), click the **Keep** button, input the corresponding molarity of the solution in the cuvet in the appearing dialog box. Press **OK** for next one.

4. Repeat the same procedure for all the other nine copper solutions you prepared.

5. When all the measurements are done, press **Stop** button choose Autoscale, and **save** the data.

6. Do the second trial as before. Select **Store Latest Run** from the **Experiment** menu. This will store your first data set as Run 1. In the second trial you do not need to prepare new solutions; just use the solutions you prepared in part I to get the second set of readings.

7. Select the points which comply with Beer's Law and click the **Linear Fit** button. Select **Run 1** and **Latest**. Place the boxes for the linear fits where they do not interfere with the data.

8. Determine ε from each graph where the path length equals 1.0 cm. Determine the mean value of ε for your two trials. Title and save the graph. Leave the graph open for Part III.

Part III—Determination of the Concentration of an Unknown Solution

1. Your instructor will assign you one of three unknown solutions. Use a 50 mL beaker to obtain approximately 20 mL of your assigned unknown solution and record the ID code on Data Sheet II.

2. Using the same method as in Part I, prepare three dilutions of the unknown by measuring 3.00 mL, 4.00 mL and 5.00 mL of unknown with an automatic pipet, adding 10 mL of deionized water and 2.50 mL of 2.5*M* ammonia solution to each sample, and diluting to 25.00 mL using your volumetric flasks.

3. On your standard plot from Part II, increase the number of significant figures of the concentration value to 5 by selecting "concentration" from **"Column Options"** in the **"Data"** menu. Under the **Options** tab, adjust "Displayed Precision" to 4 significant figures. Repeat for the "absorbance" column.

4. Measure absorbance of the three dilutions of your unknown solution without collecting the data points and record the values manually on data sheet II.

5. Open the **interpolation calculator** function from the **analyze** menu, choose the linear fit with the best correlation, input the absorbance of your first dilution and record the corresponding concentration. Repeat this step for the absorbances from the other two dilutions. Place the boxes for the interpolation calculator where they do not interfere with data and print your graph.

6. Use these three concentrations of your dilutions to calculate the original concentration of the unknown solution.

Print Name: _____ Date: _____ Lab Bench #: _____

DATA SHEET I

- Show a sample calculation for each type of calculated value.

Molarity of $CuSO_4$ solution _____ *M*   *1st*   *2nd*

Solution Number	Volume CuSO₄ for dilution	Molarity, calculated	%T	A	%T	A
1	_____	_____	___	___	___	___
2	_____	_____	___	___	___	___
3	_____	_____	___	___	___	___
4	_____	_____	___	___	___	___
5	_____	_____	___	___	___	___
6	_____	_____	___	___	___	___
7	_____	_____	___	___	___	___
8	_____	_____	___	___	___	___
9	_____	_____	___	___	___	___
10	_____	_____	___	___	___	___
11	_____	_____	___	___	___	___
12	_____	_____	___	___	___	___

Value of   from graph   _____   _____

Mean Value   _____

DATA SHEET II

- Show a sample calculation for each type of calculated value.

  Code for Unknown   _____

  Volume of unknown used   _____   _____   _____

  A of three unknown dilutions   _____   _____   _____

  Concentration of dilutions   _____   _____   _____

  Concentration of unknown   _____   _____   _____

  Mean concentration of unknown   _____

Post-Laboratory Questions

1. Explain why an object whose color is purple actually absorbs visible light in the green wavelength region.

2. If the concentration of an unknown solution we were studying in a Beer's Law experiment were higher than the range of concentrations used to prepare the standard plot, suggest how we could determine its concentration.

3. A solution containing 0.010 moles of some complex ion in 100.0 mL of solution was observed to transmit 65.0% of the incident light compared to an appropriate blank. (a) What is the absorbance of the solution at this wavelength? (b) What percentage of light would be transmitted by a solution four times as concentrated?

4. A sample in a 1.0 cm cell is determined to transmit 80.0% of the light at a fixed wavelength. If the molar absorptivity of this substance at this wavelength is 2.3 cm^{-1}M^{-1}, what is the concentration of the substance?

5. (a) What are the factors that could lead to deviations from Beer's Law? (b) Name at least three factors that could lead to experimental errors in the measurements made in this experiment.

BEFORE YOU COME TO LAB YOU MUST COMPLETE A PRELAB ASSIGNMENT:

Experiment 10: Transition Metal Complexes and Beer's Law Online PRELAB Quiz:

- The online Transition Metal Complexes and Beer's Law PRELAB Quiz is composed of multiple choice questions.
- The PRELAB score accounts for 40 points of your total lab score.
- The PRELAB quiz is timed, and it must be submitted before **11:59pm the night before your experiment.**
- You may only submit the PRELAB quiz once.
- In order to prepare for your PRELAB quiz, it is recommended that you study the background information, calculations, and lab procedure for the experiment in your lab manual. You may be asked to perform calculations; the correct answer will need to be reported to the proper number of significant figures and with the appropriate units.
- You may be asked to prepare and print out a graph that you will turn into your instructors when you come to lab.

11

Determining the Universal Gas Constant by the Decomposition of Hydrogen Peroxide

BACKGROUND INFORMATION

The Gas Laws

Depending on temperature and pressure, most substances can exist as a solid, a liquid, or a gas. The phase is in part determined by the strength of the intermolecular forces acting between particles. The forces in a solid are strong and the molecules are held rigidly in place; thus a solid has a fixed shape regardless of the shape of its container. In a liquid the particles are still held closely together, but the intermolecular forces do not hold the molecules together as strongly compared to a solid. The molecules are able to slide past each other, and, although the volume of a liquid is fixed, it will conform to the shape of a container.

Gases differ from liquids and solids because their constituent particles are free to move without restraint. The particles of a gas are far apart compared to their size. Since the forces between molecules diminish in strength with distance, the intermolecular forces between gas particles are nearly negligible. Thus, we observe that gases expand when given the opportunity, while condensed phases (liquids and solids) do not. Gases are highly compressible while liquids and solids are not. The particles of liquids and solids are already close together, and therefore applying pressure has little effect on their volume.

As the intermolecular forces between gas particles become truly insignificant and as the particles become so small that they seldom collide, gases behave more identically. This is reasonable; if particles have no influence upon each other, then the type of particles will not matter. As the intermolecular forces become more and more negligible, this common gas that all gases come to resemble is called an **Ideal Gas**.

The behavior of an ideal gas tends to be simple. To understand the behavior we must answer a few questions:

1. How many particles are present?
2. How much space do they travel in?
3. How fast are they traveling?
4. When they meet the container wall, what force prevents further travel?

These questions are answered by the values of these variables:

1. n, the number of moles
2. V, the volume of the container

3. T, the absolute temperature in Kelvin; K, a measure of the kinetic energy

4. P, the pressure or force per unit area

Historically, several scientists studied and determined the relationships between volume and the three other variables.

In the 17th century Robert Boyle studied the relationship between the volume and pressure of a gas and found that the pressure of a sample of gas held at constant temperature is inversely proportional to its volume. As pressure increases, the volume the gas occupies will decrease.

- $P \propto \dfrac{1}{v}$ if n and T are held constant (**Boyle's Law**)

$$V \times P = constant \quad or \quad P_1V_1 = P_2V_2 \qquad \text{Eq. 11.1}$$

In the early 19th century, Jacques Charles and Joseph Gay-Lussac studied the relationship between gas temperature and volume. Jaques Charles found that for a fixed sample of gas at a fixed pressure, the volume of gas is proportional to its temperature.

- $V \propto T$ when n and P are held constant (**Charles's Law**)

$$\dfrac{V}{T} = constant \quad or \quad \dfrac{V_1}{T_1} = \dfrac{V_2}{T_2} \qquad \text{Eq. 11.2}$$

Joseph Gay-Lussac studied the relationship of pressure and temperature in a fixed sample of gas held at constant volume and determined that pressure and temperature were directly proportional.

- $P \propto T$ if n and V are kept constant (**Gay-Lussac's Law**)

$$\dfrac{P}{T} = constant \quad or \quad \dfrac{P_1}{T_1} = \dfrac{P_2}{T_2} \qquad \text{Eq. 11.3}$$

Studying the work of Gay-Lussac and Charles, William Thompson (Lord Kelvin), used the linear relationship between an ideal gas's volume and temperature to extrapolate and devise the absolute temperature scale. In this scale, a temperature of zero would be the temperature at which a gas had zero volume. Absolute zero, 0 Kelvin, is equal to -273.15 °C. The linear relationship between gas volume and absolute temperature means when doing gas law calculations, you must use the Kelvin scale for temperature.

The **Combined Gas Law** is a combination of the relationships determined by these three chemists:

$$\dfrac{PV}{T} = constant \quad or \quad \dfrac{P_1V_1}{T_1} = \dfrac{P_2V_2}{T_2} \qquad \text{Eq. 11.4}$$

Avogadro studied the work of Joseph Gay-Lussac and determined that if the pressure, volume and temperature of two gas samples are the same, then the two samples must contain the same number of molecules of gas.

- $V \propto n$ if P and T are kept constant (**Avogadro's Law**)

$$\dfrac{V}{n} = constant \quad or \quad \dfrac{V_1}{n_1} = \dfrac{V_2}{n_2} \qquad \text{Eq. 11.5}$$

Combining these relationships we determine that $V \propto \dfrac{nT}{P}$

$$\dfrac{PV}{nT} = constant \quad or \quad \dfrac{P_1V_1}{n_1T_1} = \dfrac{P_2V_2}{n_2T_2} \qquad \text{Eq. 11.6}$$

Proportionality means that variables differ by a multiplicative constant. If one variable doubles, so does the other. If one variable is decreased by a factor of 10, so does the other. In the case of an ideal gas, we call that proportionality constant R. Now we can write

$$\frac{PV}{nT} = R$$

We rearrange this into the common form of the **Ideal Gas Law**:

$$PV = nRT \qquad\qquad \text{Eq. 11.7}$$

Here R, our **Universal Gas Constant** has the value $R = \dfrac{PV}{nT}$. While typically

n is measured in moles and temperature is measured in Kelvins, pressure and volume can be measured in a variety of units. The SI units for pressure and volume would be Pascals and cubic meters, respectively. Pressure could also be measured in atmospheres, torr, inches of mercury, etc. Volume is also often measured in different units (liters, milliliters, etc.). With each different set of units, the numerator of PV/nT changes while the denominator remains the same. Thus, the value of R changes with the choice of units. It is important to choose the value of R that corresponds to the units chosen to measure pressure and volume.

$$R = .082057 \, \frac{L \cdot atm}{mol \cdot K}$$

or

$$R = 8.31446 \, \frac{J}{mol \cdot K}$$

Because $Pa \cdot m^3 = \left(\dfrac{Kg}{m \cdot s^2} \right) \cdot m^3 = \dfrac{Kg \cdot m^2}{s^2} = Joules$, R is more commonly expressed

as $\dfrac{J}{mol \cdot K}$ than as $\dfrac{Pa \cdot m^3}{mol \cdot K}$ when SI units are applied.

We can convert from one value of R to the other:

$$0.082057 \, \frac{L \cdot atm}{mol \cdot K} \left(\frac{101325 \, Pa}{1 \, atm} \cdot \frac{1 m^3}{1000 \, L} \right)$$

$$= 8.31446 \, \frac{J}{mol \cdot K}$$

In terms of our experiment, we can use any gas that's behaving ideally, measure P, V, n and T, and experimentally calculate the value for the Ideal Gas Constant, R. In this experiment we'll use oxygen. Our source of oxygen gas will be the decomposition of hydrogen peroxide.

Enzyme-Catalyzed Decomposition of Peroxide

Hydrogen peroxide is stored in amber bottles because exposure to the UV light in sunlight will cause the slow decomposition of hydrogen peroxide (H_2O_2) into water and oxygen gas:

$$2H_2O_2(l) \xrightarrow{\text{uv light}} 2H_2O(l) + O_2(g) \text{ (slow)}$$

The rate of hydrogen peroxide decomposition can be significantly sped up by the addition of a catalyst. The enzyme catalase catalyzes the decomposition of peroxide quantitatively to oxygen gas (O_2):

$$2H_2O_2(l) \xrightarrow{\text{catalase}} 2H_2O(l) + O_2(g) \text{ (fast)}$$

Dried baker's yeast (along with potatoes and blood) is exceptionally rich in catalase. Contact of yeast to a solution of H_2O_2 instantly results in the rapid and immediate evolution of O_2. We will use catalase to decompose a measured amount of H_2O_2 in a closed system designed to allow us to measure the amount of O_2 generated.

Since we know the stoichiometric relationship of the decomposition of hydrogen peroxide, we can decompose a measured amount of hydrogen peroxide and determine the number of moles of oxygen produced by the reaction.

The Universal Gas Constant can be calculated from the number of moles of O_2 produced, the temperature, the volume, and the pressure of the gas. This will be the goal of this laboratory experiment.

SAMPLE CALCULATIONS

Pressure of the O_2 Collected

We will use a leveling-bulb assembly (see Figure 11.1) to ensure that the pressure of gas collected will be equal to the atmospheric pressure in the lab. The atmospheric pressure in the lab will be provided to you. Units of pressure can be converted given the following relationships:

$$1.000 \text{ in. Hg} = 25.40 \text{ torr}$$
$$1.000 \text{ atmosphere} = 760.0 \text{ torr}$$

Along with the O_2 collected in our closed system, there will also be a small amount of water vapor. Water vapor mixes with the oxygen gas because the oxygen is in contact with water. Dalton's Law of Partial Pressures states that in a mixture of unreacting gases, the total pressure will be the sum of the partial pressures of each individual gas. Applying Dalton's Law we can determine the total pressure in the closed system:

$$P_{Total} = P_{water} + P_{oxygen}$$

Using the leveling bulb, we can be sure that the pressure inside our closed system will equal the external atmospheric pressure of the lab. Therefore, the sum of the pressures of our oxygen gas and water vapor in our closed system will be equal to the atmospheric pressure. The pressure of water vapor is temperature dependent—a table of temperature-specific water vapor pressures can be found in Appendix III.5.

$$P_{Total} = P_{atmospheric} = P_{water} + P_{oxygen} \qquad \text{Eq. 11.8}$$

By rearranging this expression we can determine the pressure of the oxygen gas given the water vapor pressure and atmospheric pressure.

EXAMPLE:

If the atmospheric pressure in the lab is 31 in. of Hg and the temperature of the gas collected is 25°C

$$P_{atmospheric} = (31.0 \text{ in Hg}) \times (25.4 \text{ torr/in Hg}) = 787.4 \text{ torr}$$

$$P_{water} (@25°C) = 23.8 \text{ torr}$$

$$P_{oxygen} = P_{atm} - P_{water} = 787.4 - 23.8 = 763.3 \text{ torr} = 763 \text{ torr}$$

Moles of O_2 Generated

Assuming that the apparatus we are using will be airtight, the number of moles of H_2O_2 that are decomposed is stoichiometrically related to the number of moles of O_2 that will be collected. We start by computing the mass of the H_2O_2 solution used:

$$\text{mass } H_2O_2 \text{ solution} = (\text{volume } H_2O_2 \text{ soln}) \times (\text{density } H_2O_2 \text{ soln}) \qquad \text{Eq. 11.9}$$

Next, given the percent H_2O_2 in the solution by mass (typically indicated as % g/g or % wt/wt), we can compute the mass of H_2O_2 used:

$$\text{mass of } H_2O_2 = (\text{volume of } H_2O_2 \text{ soln}) \times \left(\frac{\text{\# g of } H_2O_2}{1.000\text{g solution}} \right)$$

The number of moles of H_2O_2 can now be computed from the mass of the H_2O_2 used in the reaction and the molar mass of H_2O_2:

$$\text{moles of } H_2O_2 \text{ reacted} = (\text{mass of } H_2O_2) \times \left(\frac{1 \text{ mol of } H_2O_2}{34.02 \text{ g } H_2O_2} \right) \quad \text{Eq. 11.10}$$

Given the stoichiometry of the reaction we can determine that the ratio of the number of moles of H_2O_2 decomposing to the number of moles of O_2 produced is 2 to 1:

$$\text{moles of } O_2 \text{ produced} = (\text{moles of } H_2O_2 \text{ reacted}) \times \left(\frac{1 \text{ mol } O_2}{2 \text{ mol of } H_2O_2} \right) \quad \text{Eq. 11.11}$$

EXAMPLE:

5.00 mL of a 5.00% (g/g) solution of H_2O_2 with density of 1.01 g/mL are used. The moles of O_2 generated can be found by:

$$\text{mass of } H_2O_2 \text{ solution} = (5.00\text{mL}) \times \left(1.01\frac{g}{mL} \right) = 5.05\text{g}$$

$$\text{mass of } H_2O_2 \text{ solution} = (5.05\text{g}) \times \left(\frac{0.0500 \text{ g of } H_2O_2}{1.000 \text{ g solution}} \right) = 0.253\text{g } H_2O_2$$

$$\text{moles of } H_2O_2 \text{ reacted} = (0.253\text{g } H_2O_2) \times \left(\frac{1\text{mol of } H_2O_2}{34.02 \text{ g } H_2O_2} \right) = 7.42 \times 10^{-3} \text{ mol } H_2O_2$$

$$\text{moles of } O_2 \text{ produced} = (7.42 \times 10^{-3}\text{mol } H_2O_2) \times \left(\frac{1 \text{ mol } O_2}{2 \text{ mol } H_2O_2} \right) = 3.71 \times 10^{-3} \text{ mol } O_2$$

Temperature and Volume

Volume will be reported in Liters and measured by water displacement in a buret. Temperature will be measured with your thermometer, but should be noted in Kelvins (K) and not degrees Celsius for your calculations.

$$K = 273.15 + °C \qquad \text{Eq. 11.12}$$

Experimental Error

Relative experimental error is defined as the difference between the actual value and the experimental result divided by the actual value.

$$\%\text{Error} = \left| \frac{(\text{actual} - \text{experimental})}{\text{actual}} \right| \times 100\% \qquad \text{Eq. 11.13}$$

PURPOSE

1. Measure the amount of O_2 generated from the decomposition of H_2O_2.

2. Calculate the Universal Gas Constant.

INSTRUMENTATION AND EQUIPMENT

The apparatus that will be used in this experiment to measure the amount of gas evolution is shown in Figure 11.1.

Assembling the Apparatus

1. Obtain all the equipment in Figure 11.1 below from your lab instructor.
2. Clamp a clean 50mL buret to the support stand. Next, clamp a clean and dry 25 mm test tube to the support stand. They should be positioned so that the rubber tubing between the two hole No. 4 rubber stopper and one hole No. 00 rubber stopper will reach between the test tube and the top of the buret.

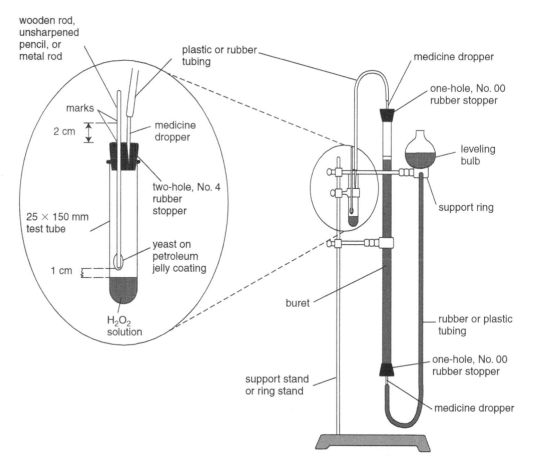

Figure 11.1 Measuring the volume of O_2 produced from the decomposition of H_2O_2 in a closed system

3. Take the wooden rod, lubricate the bottom 2cm of the rod with petroleum jelly, and insert it into one hole of the two-hole No. 4 rubber stopper. Move the rod back and forth in the hole to ensure that it is properly lubricated and airtight.
4. Adjust the rod so that the end touches the bottom of the test tube. Mark the location of the rod above the stopper with a pen. Withdraw the wooden rod 2cm and make a second mark above the stopper. This will allow you to replace the wooden rod at the appropriate height so as not to start the reaction prematurely.
5. Clamp the clean 50mL buret to the support stand.
6. Attach a ring support to the support stand. Place the leveling bulb into the support and insert the stopper at the other end of the long tubing tightly into the bottom of the buret.

7. Fill the buret barrel with deionized water until and the water level in the buret is at the 0.0 mark and the leveling bulb is approximately half full.

8. Move the leveling bulb up and down until the water levels in the buret and bulb are aligned. Fix the ring support to keep the bulb at this level. Check to make sure that there are no air bubbles or leaks present.

9. Attach the stopper to the top of the buret. Your assembly is now ready for the experiment.

PROCEDURE

> **Chemical Hazards**
>
> • 3% Hydrogen Peroxide: May cause eye, skin, and respiratory tract irritation.
>
> Care should be taken when working with these reagents. Avoid inhalation and contact with skin, eyes, and clothing. Goggles, gloves, and lab coats are required at all times.

This procedure should be followed carefully. Perform two or three trials as instructed by your lab instructor.

Part I—Catalyzed Decomposition of Hydrogen Peroxide with Yeast

1. You will be using an automatic pipet. This piece of equipment is very delicate, so please review Appendix III before use. Some things to keep in mind as you use the automatic pipet:
   • NEVER lay the pipet on its side, always return the pipet to a pipet stand when not in use to avoid damage to the pipet.
   • Practice using the pipet before performing the experiment; ask your instructor if you have any questions.
   • Do not set volumes outside the pipet's volume range.
   • REFER to Appendix III for instructions on using the automatic pipet.

2. Remove the rubber stopper assembly with the rod and tube from the test tube and the top of the buret.

3. Pipet 3.00mL of the H_2O_2 solution directly into the test tube. It is now critical that yeast not come in contact with the solution, or the reaction will begin prematurely.

4. Before replacing the rubber stopper into the test tube, place a small amount of petroleum jelly on the bottom tip of the rod. Gently place the rod in a small amount of baker's yeast. Tap the rod gently to make sure that the yeast will not fall off.

Again: Any loose yeast falling into the peroxide prematurely will necessitate repeating the procedure from the beginning.

5. Carefully replace the stopper into the test tube.

6. Perform one last check for leaks or air bubbles before proceeding. Move the leveling bulb up and down, finally stopping with the water level in the buret at 0.00mL. Reconnect the stopper to the top of the buret and clamp the bulb in place.

7. Now record the actual initial volume in the buret to the nearest hundredth of a milliliter.

8. Slowly depress the rod into the peroxide solution. The reaction will begin instantaneously. As the oxygen is released, the water level will begin to drop in the buret. Unclamp and move the leveling bulb as the reaction runs so that the water levels are approximately equal

9. When you can no longer see any bubbling in the peroxide solution (at least 5 minutes after starting the reaction), loosen the clamp on the test tube and agitate lightly. If the water level does not change, re-clamp the test tube and withdraw the rod to its original location; use a gentle, slow, twisting motion.

10. Adjust the leveling bulb until the water levels in the buret and the bulb are precisely aligned. Record the buret reading to the nearest 0.01mL.

11. Insert a thermometer into the leveling bulb and determine the temperature of the water immediately at the end of the reaction.

Part II—Determining R, the Universal Gas Constant

1. Obtain the atmospheric pressure in the lab and density of the hydrogen peroxide solution. (Provided by instructor)

2. Use the data collected to experimentally determine the Universal Gas Constant. Complete Data Sheets I and II.

DATA SHEET I

- Show a sample calculation for each type of calculated value.

CONSTANTS

Atmospheric Pressure _____ in. Hg _____ torr

Density of H_2O_2 Solution _____ g/mL

Mass Percent of H_2O_2 solution _____ g H_2O_2/1.0g Solution

DECOMPOSITION OF HYDROGEN PEROXIDE

Moles of O_2

	Trial 1	Trial 2	Trial 3
Volume of H_2O_2	_____	_____	_____
Mass of H_2O_2 soln	_____	_____	_____
Mass of H_2O_2	_____	_____	_____
Moles of H_2O_2	_____	_____	_____
Moles of O_2	_____	_____	_____

Volume of O_2

	Trial 1	Trial 2	Trial 3
Initial Buret Reading	_____	_____	_____
Final Buret Reading	_____	_____	_____
Volume of O_2 collected	_____	_____	_____
Temperature of water	_____	_____	_____

Pressure of O_2

	Trial 1	Trial 2	Trial 3
Water Vapor Pressure	_____	_____	_____
Pressure of O_2 collected	_____	_____	_____

DATA SHEET II

- Show a sample calculation for each type of calculated value.

   Results—*Universal Gas Constant*

	Trial 1	*Trial 2*	*Trial 3*
Calculated R, L · atm/mol · K	_____	_____	_____
Mean Value			_____
Percent Error			_____

Post-Laboratory Questions

1. Compare the calculated value of R to the actual value of $0.08205 \dfrac{L \cdot atm}{mol \cdot K}$

   For each of your trials, if your observed value was higher/lower than the actual value, suggest possible error that may have contributed to this difference. Support your arguments using the form of the ideal gas law: $R = \dfrac{PV}{nT}$

2. A series of errors were encountered in doing this experiment. What result would each have caused on the calculation of R? Would the value computed be too high, too low, or unaffected? Support your answers with calculations.

   a. The density and mass percent of the H_2O_2 solution were 1.10g/mL and 4.591% (wt/wt) instead of the 1.01g/mL and 5.00% (wt/wt) that you were told.

   b. The H_2O_2 solution was left out over the weekend in a clear container. You take lab first thing Monday morning and use the concentration written on the bottle in your calculations. Use the Ideal Gas Law to support your answer.

   c. The student read the atmospheric pressure, 30.2 in Hg, off of a second blackboard in the lab that corresponded to yesterday's pressure. Today's atmospheric pressure is actually 759.0mm of Hg. Support with calculations.

d. The student forgot to measure the temperature of the water immediately after the reaction had completed. Three minutes later, the temperature was found to be 24.5°C. If the water cools at a rate of 0.2 degrees per minute, what would the effect be?

e. The student forgot to take into account water vapor pressure in the system when doing their calculations.

3. When studying gases, chemists use a set of standard conditions called Standard Temperature and Pressure (STP) defined as 0° C and 1 atm. What is the molar volume of the O_2 gas at STP? If we were collecting H_2 instead of O_2, what would the molar volume be at STP? Explain.

BEFORE YOU COME TO LAB YOU MUST COMPLETE A PRELAB ASSIGNMENT:

Experiment 11: Determining the Universal Gas Constant by the Decomposition of Hydrogen Peroxide PRELAB Quiz:

- The online Determining the Universal Gas Constant PRELAB Quiz is composed of multiple choice questions.
- The PRELAB score accounts for 40 points of your total lab score.
- The PRELAB quiz is timed, and it must be submitted before **11:59pm the night before your experiment.**
- You may only submit the PRELAB quiz once.
- In order to prepare for your PRELAB quiz, it is recommended that you study the background information, calculations, and lab procedure for the experiment in your lab manual. You may be asked to perform calculations; the correct answer will need to be reported to the proper number of significant figures and with the appropriate units.
- You may be asked to prepare and print out a graph that you will turn into your instructors when you come to lab.

12

Measuring Gas Evolution: Stoichiometry of the Reaction of Magnesium with Hydrochloric Acid

BACKGROUND INFORMATION

In any reaction a relationship exists between the number of moles of each of the species in the reaction. In stoichiometry, we study that relationship to create a balanced chemical equation.

The number of moles of any species consumed or evolved in a reaction is proportional to its coefficient in the balanced chemical equation. For species A, B and C involved in a reaction we can write

$$\frac{n_A}{\text{coefficient}_A} = \frac{n_B}{\text{coefficient}_B} = \frac{n_C}{\text{coefficient}_C} \qquad \text{Eq. 12.1}$$

where n_A is the number of moles of "A," and coefficient_A is the coefficient of that species in the balanced chemical equation. A similar relationship exists for species B and C. If we know the number of moles of one species, we can calculate the number of moles for any species, given the balanced chemical equation.

When a metal (M) reacts with a strong acid, such as hydrochloric acid, the products are a cation of the metal and hydrogen gas (H_2).

$$M_{(s)} + x\, H_3O^+_{(aq)} \rightarrow M^{x+}_{(aq)} + x/2\, H_{2(g)} + xH_2O_{(l)} \qquad \text{Eq. 12.2}$$

Here x is related to the oxidation state of the metal and the appropriate number of moles of acid that will react with that specific metal in question.

This experiment involves the reaction of a measured amount of magnesium metal (Mg) with a known, but excess amount of hydrochloric acid—$HCl_{(aq)}$. $Mg_{(s)}$ and $HCl_{(aq)}$ react to form H_2 gas. The process involves a redox reaction between $Mg_{(s)}$ & $HCl_{(aq)}$. Electrons from Mg are transferred to $H_3O^+_{(aq)}$ to form H_2 gas and water. Mg is oxidized (loses electrons) while the hydrogen is reduced (gains electrons). The transfer of electrons must be balanced:

$$Mg_{(s)} \rightarrow Mg^{2+}_{(aq)} + 2e^- \text{ (oxidation)}$$

$$2H_3O^+_{(aq)} + 2e^- \rightarrow H_{2(g)} + 2H_2O_{(l)} \text{ (reduction)}$$

The stoichiometry of the reaction will be determined by two different analytical methods, measuring gas evolution and back-titration.

153

We start with a measured amount of magnesium metal and add an excess but known amount of hydrochloric acid. We assume that magnesium, as the limiting reagent, reacts to completion. Therefore, given the molar mass of the magnesium metal, we can determine the number of moles consumed in the reaction.

The volume of H_2 gas evolved in the experiment displaces the same volume of water from a container. Using Dalton's Law and the Ideal Gas Law (see background information in Chapter 11), we use the amount of displaced water to calculate the number of moles of H_2 generated in the reaction.

After the magnesium is consumed, the reaction mixture is then titrated with standardized sodium hydroxide to determine the amount of unreacted hydrochloric acid. From this, the moles of $HCl_{(aq)}$ that were consumed in the reaction with magnesium are calculated by subtracting the moles of unreacted $HCl_{(aq)}$ from the initial moles of $HCl_{(aq)}$.

We can then use these molar amounts to experimentally determine the stoichiometric ratios for the reaction of magnesium with hydrochloric acid.

SAMPLE CALCULATIONS

Determining the Moles of $H_{2(g)}$ Generated

Calculating the number of moles of $H_{2(g)}$ generated can be accomplished using the Ideal Gas Law (see background information in Chapter 11 for more information on the Ideal Gas Law). At room temperature and pressure, H_2 acts as an ideal gas since the gas molecules rarely interact. Given the volume, pressure, and temperature of the gas we can determine the number of moles exactly. The stoichiometry of the reaction can be inferred from this calculation.

1. Volume of H_2 generated:

   The volume of water displaced will be equal to the volume of H_2 gas generated. We measure the mass of the displaced water and use density to determine the volume. See Table IV.4 in Appendix IV for a table of the density of pure water as a function of temperature.

$$\text{volume of } H_2 = \frac{(\text{mass of water displaced, g})}{\left(\text{density of water, } \frac{g}{mL}\right)} \qquad \text{Eq. 12.3}$$

2. Pressure of the H_2 generated:

   The total gas pressure in the closed collection system is equal to the sum of the constituent partial pressures (this is Dalton's Law of partial pressures). Because the hydrogen gas is in contact with water, water vapor will evolve along with the hydrogen gas. Therefore, according to Dalton's Law:

$$P_{Total} = P_{H_2O} + P_{H_2}$$

   We will equalize the water levels in the collection beaker (which is open to atmospheric pressure) and the closed system. At this point, with the water levels equal, the pressure inside the collection system is equal to the atmospheric pressure.

$$P_{Total} = P_{ATM} = P_{H_2O} + P_{H_2}$$

or

$$P_{H_2} = P_{ATM} - P_{H_2O} \qquad \text{Eq. 12.4}$$

where P_{ATM} is the atmospheric pressure in the laboratory at the time of the experiment and P_{H_2O} is the water vapor pressure which is dependent on the temperature of the water in the filter flask. See Table IV.3 in the Appendix IV for a table of water vapor pressures as a function of temperature.

3. Number of moles of H_2 collected during the reaction:

   To determine the number of moles of H_2 gas, we use the Ideal Gas Law

$$n = \frac{PV}{RT} \qquad \text{Eq. 12.5}$$

where P is the pressure of the gas in atmospheres; V is the volume of the gas in liters; R is the molar gas constant, $.082057 \frac{L \cdot atm}{mol \cdot K}$; and T is the temperature of the water in the filtering flask in Kelvins. Because the gas collected is in contact with the water in the filtering flask, this will more accurately represent the temperature of the gas than the room temperature.

Determining the Moles of Mg(*s*) Consumed in the Reaction

Magnesium is the limiting reagent and the $HCl_{(aq)}$ in excess, therefore all the magnesium is consumed.

$$\text{Moles of magnesium consumed in reaction} = \frac{(\text{mass of magnesium, g})}{\left(\text{molar mass of magnesium, } \frac{g}{mol}\right)}$$

$$\text{Eq. 12.6}$$

Determining the Moles of HCl(*aq*) Consumed in the Reaction

Here we cannot directly titrate the $HCl_{(aq)}$ that reacts with the magnesium, but instead we titrate the $HCl_{(aq)}$ remaining after the reaction with Mg to determine the moles of $HCl_{(aq)}$ that did not react with Mg. This is called back-titration. Since a known but excess amount of $HCl_{(aq)}$ was reacted with magnesium, we can subtract the number of moles left after the reaction (determined by our titration) from the initial moles of acid to deduce how many moles of acid did react with the magnesium.

1. Number of moles of $HCl_{(aq)}$ initially added to reaction vessel:

   Initial moles $HCl_{(aq)}$ = (volume $HCl_{(aq)}$, L) × (concentration of $HCl_{(aq)}$, M)   Eq. 12.7

2. Number of moles of $HCl_{(aq)}$ solution titrated in the back-titration:

   Moles of $HCl_{(aq)}$ titrated = moles of $NaOH_{(aq)}$ titrated = (volume $NaOH_{(aq)}$, L)
   × (concentration $NaOH_{(aq)}$, M)   Eq. 12.8

3. Moles $HCl_{(aq)}$ used in the reaction with magnesium:

   Moles $HCl_{(aq)}$ reacting with $Mg_{(s)}$ = (initial moles $HCl_{(aq)}$) − (moles HCl solution
   titrated in back-titration)   Eq. 12.9

PURPOSE

1. Measure gas evolution in a chemical reaction
2. Determine the stoichiometry of the reaction between magnesium and hydrochloric acid

INSTRUMENTATION AND EQUIPMENT

1. Analytical balance
2. Top loading balance
3. Siphon assembly

Two different types of balances will be used in the experiment. The measurements of the magnesium turnings have to be done to the nearest 0.0001 g. Only the analytical balances are capable of delivering this level of precision. The beakers of displaced water tend to be too heavy for use with the analytical balance and will therefore be weighed with top loading balances. These weights should be measured to the nearest centigram (0.01 g). Although we are using multiple balances, be consistent. All analytical measurements should be made with the same analytical balance. The same applies to the measurements made with the top loading balances.

The siphon assembly, and its setup, are crucial to the success of this experiment and are discussed in the first section of the procedure.

Assembling the Apparatus

Carefully assemble the apparatus depicted below in Figure 12.1 consisting of a 125 mL Erlenmeyer flask, a 500 mL filter flask, a 150mL beaker, and various glass tubing and rubber hoses. Remove the stopper from the filter flask and fill it 3/4 way full with deionized water. Add 75–100 mL of water to the beaker.

Replace the stopper with the glass tubing into the 500 mL filter flask. Submerge the other end of the tubing in the 75–100 mL of water in the collection beaker. Now remove the stopper from the 125 mL Erlenmeyer flask. Make sure the other end of the tubing is secured to the arm of the 500 mL filter flask. Using an atomizer bulb, carefully blow air through the stopper that was in the Erlenmeyer reaction flask. This will increase the pressure in the filter flask and force water through the glass tubing and into the collection beaker, creating a siphon system.

Keeping the tubing in the collection beaker submerged, raise and lower the beaker so that water flows back and forth from the filter flask and all air bubbles are removed. Once the siphon is intact and you are convinced that the system is airtight, attach the screw clamp to the siphon. This will prevent any premature water flow.

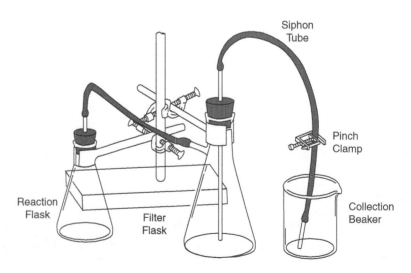

Figure 12.1   Apparatus for the experiment

PROCEDURE

This procedure should be followed carefully. Perform two or three trials as instructed by your lab instructor.

> **Chemical Hazards:**
> - 1M Hydrochloric Acid: Toxic and Corrosive. May cause eye, skin, and respiratory tract irritation.
> - 0.5M Sodium Hydroxide: Toxic and Corrosive. May cause eye, skin, and respiratory tract irritation.
> - Hydrogen gas is flammable and poses a fire and explosive hazard when concentration exceeds 4%.
>
> Care should be taken when working with these reagents. Avoid inhalation and contact with skin, eyes, and clothing. Goggles, gloves, and lab coats are required at all times.

Part I—Reaction of Magnesium with Hydrochloric Acid

Note: Do not handle the vials with your hands. It is important that the weight measurements be as accurate as possible. Place a piece of tissue or paper around the vial when handling.

1. Replace the collection beaker used to create your siphon with an empty, dry and 150 mL beaker that has been weighed on a top loading balance. Record the weight of this dry collection beaker on Data Sheet I.

2. Obtain a clean and dry vial. Using an analytical balance, accurately weigh on weighing paper between 0.050 and 0.060 g of magnesium to the nearest 0.0001 g and transfer the magnesium to the vial. ***Do not*** use a top loading balance, accuracy is very important. Do not exceed 0.060 g of magnesium.

3. Using a 25 mL volumetric pipet, add 25.00 mL of 1.00*M* hydrochloric acid to the 125 mL Erlenmeyer flask.

4. Carefully insert the vial into the 125 mL Erlenmeyer flask. Do not let it tip over until you are ready to initiate the reaction. Replace the stopper in the 125 mL Erlenmeyer flask to make your collection system airtight.

5. Release the clamp that is securing the 125 mL Erlenmeyer flask to the stand and agitate so that the vial with the magnesium tips over and the reaction begins. As soon as this occurs, the screw clamp on the tubing should be released allowing water to flow into the collection beaker. If this is not done with enough speed, the pressure build-up will cause the seals to break.

6. Continue to agitate and swirl the reaction flask until all the magnesium has been reacted. This should take approximately 15 minutes. The reaction you have just performed is exothermic. Consequently, you must allow the reaction vessel and the contents to cool to room temperature for 5 minutes before proceeding with the lab.

7. Take the collection beaker and gently raise it until the water levels in the beaker and the filter flask are approximately the same (this equalizes the pressure in the closed system to the atmospheric pressure in the lab). Refasten the screw clamp to the tubing so that the siphon remains intact for the next trial(s).

8. Weigh the beaker and displaced water to the nearest .01 g using a top loading balance.

9. Check your system before proceeding to your next trial and recreate your siphon system if necessary. **Do not discard the contents of your Erlenmeyer flask!**

10. Using your thermometer, determine the temperature of the water in the filter flask. Find the associated water vapor pressure from Table IV.3 in the back of your lab manual. The atmospheric pressure will be provided by your laboratory instructor.

Part II—Titrating the Reaction Mixture

1. Rinse and fill a clean 50 mL buret with a 0.500*M* solution of NaOH. Note the precise concentration of the base on your Data Sheet. A proper rinse procedure consists of adding 3.5 mL portions of base to the buret, rinsing, and draining through the tip. See Appendix III for a complete discussion of buret preparation.

2. Fill the buret to the calibration mark with the standardized NaOH solution. Record the levels on the buret to the nearest 0.01 mL.

3. Take the reaction Erlenmeyer flask from the previous section of the experiment (do not remove the vial) and add four drops of bromophenol blue indicator solution to the flask.

4. Titrate the reaction mixture with the NaOH solution. Use a magnetic stirrer and a stirring bar. Slowly add small amounts of base at a drop rate of 1 drop/sec. The indicator will turn the solution purple as the mixture approaches the endpoint of the titration. Continue adding smaller and smaller amounts of base until the purple color persists for more than 30 seconds.

5. Record the level of the NaOH in the buret to the nearest 0.01 mL at the equivalence point.

DATA SHEET I

CONSTANTS

- To maintain accuracy, use the same analytical balance and same top loading balance throughout this experiment.
- Water vapor pressure is temperature dependent. Obtain the correct value for the current lab temperature from your thermometer.
- Show a sample calculation for each type of calculated value.

Atmospheric Pressure _____ inches of Hg _____ torr

REACTION OF Mg$_{(s)}$ AND HCl$_{(aq)}$

	Trial 1	Trial 2	Trial 3
Mass of Mg$_{(s)}$	_____	_____	_____
Volume HCl$_{(aq)}$ added to flask	_____	_____	_____
Conc of HCl$_{(aq)}$ added to flask	_____	_____	_____
Moles of HCl$_{(aq)}$ added to flask	_____	_____	_____
Mass of beaker	_____	_____	_____
Mass of beaker + water	_____	_____	_____
Mass of displaced water	_____	_____	_____
Temperature of water in filter flask	_____	_____	_____
Water Vapor Pressure	_____	_____	_____

AMOUNT OF HYDROGEN GENERATED

	Trial 1	*Trial 2*	*Trial 3*
Volume of $H_{2(g)}$ collected	_____	_____	_____
Pressure of $H_{2(g)}$ collected	_____	_____	_____
Moles of $H_{2(g)}$ collected	_____	_____	_____

DATA SHEET II

- Show a sample calculation for each type of calculated value.

TITRATION OF REACTION MIXTURE

	Trial 1	*Trial 2*	*Trial 3*
Molarity of $NaOH_{(aq)}$	_____	_____	_____
Initial Buret reading	_____	_____	_____
Final Buret reading	_____	_____	_____
Volume of $NaOH_{(aq)}$ added	_____	_____	_____
Moles of $HCl_{(aq)}$ titrated after reaction with $Mg_{(s)}$	_____	_____	_____
Moles of $HCl_{(aq)}$ reacting with $Mg_{(s)}$	_____	_____	_____

DATA SHEET III

• Show a sample calculation for each type of calculated value.

STOICHIOMETRY OF THE REACTION

	Trial 1	*Trial 2*	*Trial 3*
Moles of $Mg_{(s)}$	_____	_____	_____
Moles of $H_{2(g)}$ collected	_____	_____	_____
Moles of $HCl_{(aq)}$ reacting with $Mg_{(s)}$	_____	_____	_____
Ratio $H_{2(g)}$ collected to $Mg_{(s)}$ consumed	_____	_____	_____
		Average Ratio	_____
Ratio $HCl_{(aq)}$ reacting to $Mg_{(s)}$ consumed	_____	_____	_____
		Average Ratio	_____

Post-Laboratory Questions

1. a. Propose the actual balanced equation for the reaction performed in today's experiment.

   b. Using the average ratios of $H_{2(g)}$ collected and $HCl_{(aq)}$ reacting versus magnesium from your data sheets, provide the experimental reaction equation. All experimental accuracy should be maintained. (Your experimental equation may not be balanced.)

   c. Describe the possible sources of error associated with the procedures to determine each of the experimental measurements (moles of $H_{2(g)}$ and $HCl_{(aq)}$ reacting).

   d. On the basis of possible errors in the experiment, which ratio is more reliable? Consequently, which of the stoichiometric ratios is the least reliable?

2. Your laboratory instructors made a mistake and provided you with 55.2 mg of calcium turnings to react with the 25.00 mL of 1.00M HCl$_{(aq)}$. Assuming the ideal stoichiometric ratios would be observed, how many mL water would have been displaced in the reaction? What volume of 0.500M NaOH$_{(aq)}$ would have been needed to titrate the residual HCl$_{(aq)}$? (Assume STP will prevail).

3. Assuming the same molar amounts of Al$_{(s)}$, Mg$_{(s)}$, and Ca$_{(s)}$ were used in this experiment, for which would there be more H$_2$ gas evolution? For which would more HCl$_{(aq)}$ remain in the reaction flask after the reaction? Provide chemical equations to support your argument.

4. In the chemistry laboratory, gas is often collected over water. Ammonium nitrite (NH$_4$NO$_2$) decomposes upon heating to produce nitrogen gas according to the following equation:

$$NH_4NO_2(s) \rightarrow N_2(g) + 2H_2O(l)$$

If 511mL of N$_2$ gas was collected over water at 26°C and 745 torr total pressure, how many grams of NH$_4$NO$_2$ was decomposed?

BEFORE YOU COME TO LAB YOU MUST COMPLETE A PRELAB ASSIGNMENT:

Experiment 12: Measuring Gas Evolution: Stoichiometry of the Reaction of Magnesium with Hydrochloric Acid Online PRELAB Quiz:

- The Measuring Gas Evolution: Stoichiometry of the Reaction of Magnesium with Hydrochloric Acid Online PRELAB Quiz is composed of multiple choice questions.
- The PRELAB score accounts for 40 points of your total lab score.
- The PRELAB quiz is timed, and it must be submitted before **11:59 pm the night before your experiment.**
- You may only submit the PRELAB quiz once.
- In order to prepare for your PRELAB quiz, it is recommended that you study the background information, calculations, and lab procedure for the experiment in your lab manual. You may be asked to perform calculations; the correct answer will need to be reported to the proper number of significant figures and with the appropriate units.
- You may be asked to prepare and print out a graph that you will turn into your instructors when you come to lab.

13

Separation by Fractional Crystallization

BACKGROUND INFORMATION

Solution Formation and Related Issues

A *mixture* is a combination of two or more substances in which the substances retain their distinct identities. A **homogeneous** mixture is one for which the composition is uniform all the way down to the molecular level. A **solution** is an example of a homogeneous mixture. The major component of a solution is the **solvent** and the minor components are the **solutes.**

If a solution is to form, at least two substances, each of which has its own intermolecular forces, have to mix uniformly. Particles of one substance will no longer be surrounded only by their own kind but will be in close proximity to particles of other substances. Ionic and molecular solids do not change in composition when they dissolve in liquid solvents; dissolution is a physical process. The relative strengths of the forces operating between: 1) pairs of solvent particles, 2) pairs of solute particles, and 3) solute and solvent particles will govern how readily the substances will mix. There will always be a tendency for them to mix because that will increase the amount of disorder (**entropy**) in the solution.

Since force is used to separate some particles and move others closer together, work is done in the solution and energy changes must be considered. When particles of solute or particles of solvent separate from each other the process is always endothermic ($\Delta H > 0$). Conversely, the step in which the solute and solvent particles approach one another is always exothermic ($\Delta H < 0$). Applying Hess's law of heat summation, the entire solution process may be either endothermic or exothermic depending on the relative magnitude of the ΔH's, all of which depend on the relative strengths of the intermolecular forces.

If the overall process is endothermic, then it is energetically unfavorable. When this happens, it is the increase in disorder that drives the dissolution process. If the process is too endothermic, and the increase in disorder is insufficient, the solute does not dissolve.

Like Dissolves Like

In an actual dissolution process, the steps described occur simultaneously, rather than sequentially. Much of the energy needed to separate particles is provided by the energy released as solute and solvent particles approach one another. The intermolecular forces acting between: 1) pairs of solvent particles, 2) pairs of solute particles, and 3) solute and solvent particles must be comparable in strength for dissolution to occur. To be comparable in strength, the particles are likely to be of the same type.

Polar solvents will tend to dissolve polar solutes, whereas nonpolar solvents will tend to dissolve nonpolar solutes. Polar and nonpolar substances will tend not to mix, but exceptions to this rule occur where the polarities of the species are borderline. There are many ionic solids that are considered insoluble in water because there is insufficient energy available to overcome the prevailing intermolecular forces. No material is completely insoluble but the degree of solubility is extremely low.

Usually, for a given amount of solvent, there's a limit to the amount of solute that will dissolve at a given temperature. We call a solution that contains the maximum amount of solute a **saturated** solution. A solution that contains less than the maximum amount of solute is an **unsaturated** solution. Unsaturated solutions are capable of dissolving more solute. For certain substances, it is possible to form a solution that contains more solute than is present in the saturated case. We call such a solution **supersaturated.** Supersaturated solutions are unstable and solute will crystallize rapidly once a crystal lattice begins to form. Crystallization of excess solute can be initiated by adding a small "seed" crystal or sometimes can be induced by a mechanical disturbance such as stirring or scraping the sides of a glass vessel in which the solution is held.

In a saturated solution, there is a dynamic equilibrium between the *solid phase* and the *solvated phase* of the solute. The solid phase dissolves at the same rate as the solvated phase *crystallizes*. If something upsets the equilibrium and causes crystallization to take place more rapidly than solvation (by lowering temperature, for example), more solid crystal will form. When the change takes place very rapidly, a finely divided solid will form, which we refer to as a **precipitate.**

Factors Affecting Solubility

While the solubility of all solids in water is affected by temperature, it is not possible to predict what the temperature dependence will be for a given substance. The solubility of some salts increase sharply with temperature (e.g. KNO_3, $NaNO_3$), some change very little with temperature (e.g. $NaCl$, KCl), and others actually decrease as the temperature rises (e.g. $Ce_2(SO_4)_3$). Experimental results are the only reliable source of temperature/solubility dependence. Figure 13.1 shows the solubilities of some ionic solids in water as a function of temperature.

If two or more solids are mixed, we can often separate them by taking advantage of their differences in their solubilities. The mixture is dissolved into a particular solvent and then the temperature is adjusted so that one component will crystallize, but the others remain in solution. The greatly purified solid is then removed. This is known as **fractional crystallization.**

Separating the Components of a Mixture

Pure substances have a unique set of physical and chemical properties that are used for identification and classification. Differences in these properties can be used to separate the components of a mixture. Sometimes it is possible to separate the components of a mixture of solids by preferentially **dissolving** or **extracting** one of the components. This can be done if one of the solids is known to be soluble in a particular solvent at elevated temperature while the other solid is not soluble. The mixture can then be separated by **decanting** (carefully pouring) the liquid portion while leaving the insoluble solid residue. We can also **filter** the residual solid through a filtering funnel on a previously

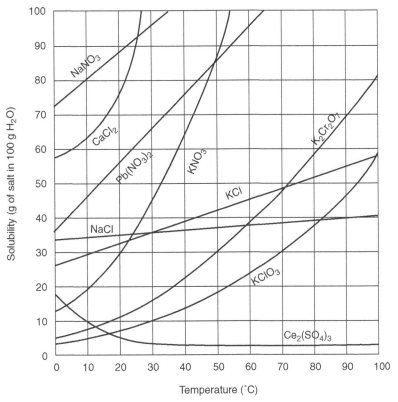

Figure 13.1 Solubilities of several ionic solids in water as a function of temperature

weighed filter paper. The residual solution or *filtrate* contains the soluble component of the mixture. After separation by filtration, the solid on the filter paper can be washed, dried, and weighed. The soluble solid in the filtrate can be recovered by *evaporation* of the solvent at a temperature high enough to drive off the solvent but not too high to melt or decompose the second component.

Consider a mixture of silver chloride (AgCl) and benzoic acid (C_6H_5COOH). Both compounds are insoluble in cold water, but only benzoic acid is soluble in hot water. If we add hot water to a AgCl-C_6H_5COOH sample of known mass and mix well, the C_6H_5COOH will dissolve and the AgCl will not. We can separate the hot mixture by decanting the liquid portion while leaving the insoluble residue, AgCl, in the beaker. By cooling the filtrate in an ice bath, the C_6H_5COOH will precipitate and can be recovered by filtering through a pre-weighed filter paper. The solid C_6H_5COOH can be recovered by carefully drying at 100°C to prevent melting or decomposition. The residual solid AgCl can be recovered by drying in a 120°C oven through evaporative drying. A flow-chart to describe this process is given on the next page (Figure 13.2).

We can calculate the mass of each recovered solid using Equation 13.1.

mass of solid, g = mass of filter paper plus solid, g − mass of filter paper, g   Eq. 13.1

We express the efficiency of the separation and recovery of the mixture of the components as the percent recovery, which we calculate using Equation 13.2.

$$\text{percent recovery}, \% = \frac{\text{mass of AgCl}, g + \text{mass of } C_6H_5COOH, g}{\text{mass of analyzed sample}, g} \times 100\%$$ Eq. 13.2

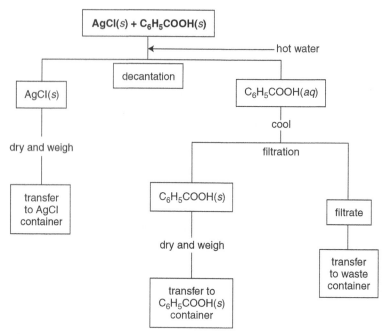

Figure 13.2   Separating AgCl and C₆H₅COOH

Fractional crystallization is an important purification and separation method along with fractional distillation, chromatography and zone refining. These processes can be utilized in the synthesis of a new substance when purification is required.

Fractional distillation is used to separate the components of a mixture (very often hydrocarbons) by boiling point differences. Chromatography utilizes minor differences in affinity for either a mobile, or stationary, phase to separate the components of a mixture with similar chemical and physical properties. Zone refining is used to segregate the contaminants from a bar of pure metal or semiconductor such as silicon. Impurities are transferred from the solid phase to the moving liquid phase as a molten zone is induced and travels from one end of the sample to the other carrying the impurities with it (because the contaminants are more soluble in the liquid phase as compared to the solid phase).

Fractional crystallization is used to separate components of a mixture that exhibit different solubility characteristics in selected solvents. Repetition of this technique can be used to purify compounds to a high degree. Consider a mixture containing potassium dichromate ($K_2Cr_2O_7$) and sodium chloride (NaCl), both of which are water-soluble ionic substances, with different solubilities at different temperatures. NaCl exhibits little change in solubility between the range of 0°C to 100°C, while $K_2Cr_2O_7$ solubility increases 16 times over the same temperature range. This property can be used to separate a mixture of the two salts from a solution.

The procedure for the separation of the mixture can be carried out as follows: Take the mixture of the salts and dissolve them in water by heating until all the solids are dissolved. Cool the solution in an ice bath until all the $K_2Cr_2O_7$ come out of solution (0°C). Separate the $K_2Cr_2O_7$ crystals by vacuum filtration using a Buchner funnel and vacuum flask (Figure 13.3). Remove the pre-weighed filter paper and dry the crystals at 110°C. Allow sample to cool prior to weighing. To recover the NaCl from the residual solution, boil away the remaining water. Allow the sample to cool and weigh the solid residue. Calculate the percent recovery of the total mixture and the percent composition of each constituent recovered.

A flow diagram for this fractional crystallization process described above is shown in Figure 13.4.

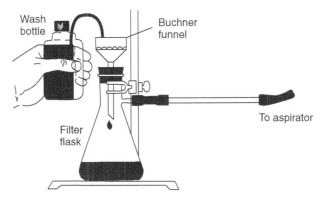

Figure 13.3 Vacuum filtration apparatus

The Experiment

The ionic salt copper(II) sulfate pentahydrate, $CuSO_4 \cdot 5H_2O$ is quite soluble in water while the organic acid, salicylic acid (2-hydroxybenzoic acid, $C_7H_6O_3$) is slightly soluble in water. The ionic salt is over 20 times more soluble than the organic acid at 0°C and nearly 100 times at 70°C. Figure 13.5 shows the solubility in water of $CuSO_4 \cdot 5H_2O$ and salicylic acid as a function of temperature. A mixture of these two solutes could be dissolved in water at 75°C to 100°C. Most of the salicylic acid could then be precipitated as fine, off-white needle-like crystals when the solution is cooled to 0°C. Up to 25–30g of $CuSO_4 \cdot 5H_2O$ per 100 g of water could remain in the cooled solution without precipitating. This procedure will be used in this experiment to separate the salicylic acid with high yield and purity.

It is harder to crystallize $CuSO_4 \cdot 5H_2O$ from water, especially if we wish to prevent the precipitation of any residual salicylic acid in solution. To obtain pure $CuSO_4 \cdot 5H_2O$ we must carefully evaporate the water from the remaining solution to about 1/4 of its original volume and then add an equal volume of 95% ethanol. The addition of the

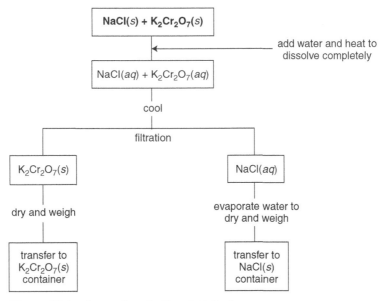

Figure 13.4 Separating NaCl and $K_2Cr_2O_7$

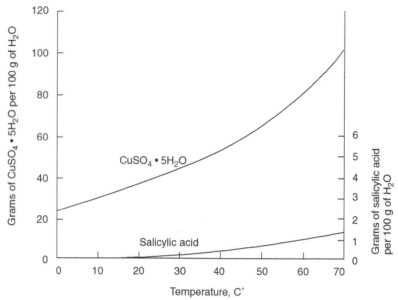

Figure 13.5   Solubility of $CuSO_4 \cdot 5H_2O$ and salicylic acid in water as a function of temperature

alcohol forces the crystallization of the $CuSO_4 \cdot 5H_2O$ since it is no longer soluble in the ethanol-water mixture♦. Essentially all of the $CuSO_4 \cdot 5H_2O$ precipitates as fine blue crystals when the solution is cooled to room temperature or lower.

Although both precipitates may appear pure, an analysis would show that the salicylic acid is contaminated by trace amounts of $CuSO_4 \cdot 5H_2O$, and vice versa. Repeating the dissolution and crystallization procedure would result in a purification of the final products. It is possible to obtain ultrapure products by repeating the process.

Water of Hydration

Evaporation of water from aqueous solutions of ionic salts will often result in hydrated ions that form stable crystals. Examples include $FeCl_3 \cdot 6H_2O$ (iron(III) chloride hexahydrate) and $CuSO_4 \cdot 5H_2O$ (copper(II) sulfate pentahydrate). This water of hydration is bound within the crystalline matrix and can be driven off by heating (usually to moderate temperatures just above the boiling point of water). For example, approximately four of the five water molecules from $CuSO_4 \cdot 5H_2O$ crystal can be removed by heating to 110°C, while removal of the last molecule will require heating to 150°C.

One can calculate how much water of hydration has been removed through heating as follows:

Calculation of X in $CuSO_4 \cdot XH_2O$:

1. Find the mass of $CuSO_4$ in the sample using the mass percent of $CuSO_4$ in $CuSO_4 \cdot 5H_2O$. The mass of $CuSO_4$ in the sample does not change as it's heated-only water is driven off during the heating process. Thus, the mass of $CuSO_4$ before and after heating is the same.

$$mass\ percent\ CuSO_4\ in\ CuSO_4 \cdot 5H_2O = \frac{molar\ mass\ CuSO_4}{molar\ mass\ CuSO_4 \cdot 5H_2O} \times 100\%$$

♦ The addition of the 95% ethanol lowers the dielectric constant of the solvent medium. The dielectric constant is the quantitative measure of the solvent's ability to decrease the force with which two oppositely charged ions attract each other. Water has a high dielectric constant and thus can solvate ionic salts into their constituent ions. The addition of an alcohol decreases this ability causing the ions to come together and precipitate.

(Initial mass of $CuSO_4 \cdot 5H_2O$) $\times$ (mass percent of $CuSO_4$ in $CuSO_4 \cdot 5H_2O$) = mass of $CuSO_4$ in $CuSO_4 \cdot 5H_2O$ sample = mass of $CuSO_4$ in $CuSO_4 \cdot XH_2O$ sample

2. Find out how much water remains in the heated, dehydrated sample of $CuSO_4 \cdot XH_2O$:

(Final mass of $CuSO_4 \cdot XH_2O$ sample) $-$ (mass of $CuSO_4$ in $CuSO_4 \cdot XH_2O$ sample) = mass of H_2O remaining in sample of $CuSO_4 \cdot XH_2O$

3. To determine X, which is a ratio of the moles of water per every mole of $CuSO_4$ in the new hydrate sample, convert the mass of $CuSO_4$ and mass of H_2O in the new hydrate to moles, and take the ratio of moles water to moles $CuSO_4$ to find X.

(mass of $CuSO_4$ in $CuSO_4 \cdot XH_2O$ in sample) $\div$ (molar mass of $CuSO_4$) = moles of $CuSO_4$ in $CuSO_4 \cdot XH_2O$ sample

(mass of H_2O remaining in sample of $CuSO_4 \cdot XH_2O$) $\div$ (molar mass of H_2O) = moles of H_2O in $CuSO_4 \cdot XH_2O$ sample

Since X is a ratio of moles of H_2O in the hydrate per mole of $CuSO_4$:

$$X = \frac{\text{(moles of } H_2O \text{ in } CuSO_4 \cdot XH_2O \text{ sample)}}{\text{(moles of } CuSO_4 \text{ in } CuSO_4 \cdot XH_2O \text{ sample)}}$$

SAMPLE CALCULATION:

A 3.857g sample of $CuSO_4 \cdot 5H_2O$ is heated in an oven at 125°C for 30 minutes. The new dehydrated sample of $CuSO_4 \cdot XH_2O$ has a mass of 2.605g. What is the value of X in the new hydrate?

1. Find the mass of $CuSO_4$ in the sample.

$$mass\ percent\ CuSO_4\ in\ CuSO_4 \cdot 5H_2O = \frac{159.62 \, {}^g\!/_{mol}\ CuSO_4}{249.70 \, {}^g\!/_{mol}\ CuSO_4 \cdot 5H_2O} \times 100\%$$

$$= 63.9247097\%$$

$$mass\ of\ CuSO_4\ in\ dehydrated\ sample = (3.857g) \times \left(\tfrac{63.9247097\%}{100\%}\right)$$

$$= 2.46557605g\ CuSO_4\ in\ CuSO_4 \cdot 5H_2O = g\ CuSO_4\ in\ CuSO_4 \cdot XH_2O$$

2. Find out how much water remains in the heated, dehydrated sample of $CuSO_4 \cdot XH_2O$:

$$mass\ H_2O\ remaining\ in\ dehydrated\ sample,\ CuSO_4 \cdot XH_2O$$

$$= (2.605g\ CuSO_4 \cdot XH_2O) - (2.46557605g\ CuSO_4)$$

$$= 0.13942395g\ H_2O\ remaining\ in\ CuSO_4 \cdot XH_2O\ sample$$

3. To determine X, which is a ratio of the moles of water per every mole of $CuSO_4$ in the new hydrate sample, convert the mass of $CuSO_4$ and mass of H_2O in the new hydrate to moles, and take the ratio of moles water to moles $CuSO_4$ to find X.

$$moles\ of\ CuSO_4\ in\ CuSO_4 \cdot XH_2O\ sample = (2.46557605g\ CuSO_4) \div \left(159.62 \, {}^g\!/_{mol}\right)$$

$$= 0.01544654\ moles\ of\ CuSO_4\ in\ CuSO_4 \cdot XH_2O\ sample$$

$$moles\ of\ H_2O\ in\ CuSO_4 \cdot XH_2O\ sample = (0.13942395g\ H_2O) \div \left(18.016 \, {}^g\!/_{mol}\right)$$

$$= 0.007389\ moles\ of\ H_2O\ in\ CuSO_4 \cdot XH_2O\ sample$$

Since X is a ratio of moles of H_2O in the hydrate per mole of $CuSO_4$:

$$X = \frac{\text{(moles of } H_2O \text{ in } CuSO_4 \cdot XH_2O \text{ sample)}}{\text{(moles of } CuSO_4 \text{ in } CuSO_4 \cdot XH_2O \text{ sample)}}$$

$$= \frac{0.0077389\ moles\ of\ H_2O}{0.01544654\ moles\ of\ CuSO_4} = 0.501001175$$

$$X = 0.501$$

PROCEDURE

Chemical Hazards
• Copper(II) Sulfate Pentahydrate: Harmful if swallowed Causes eye and skin irritation. My cause irritation to the respiratory tract. Hygroscopic.
• Salicylic Acid: May be toxic if swallowed. Causes severe eye irritation. Causes skin and eye irritation. Light sensitive.
• 3M Sulfuric Acid: Toxic. Corrosive. Harmful if inhaled or swallowed.
• 95% Ethanol: flammable liquid and vapor. Irritating to eyes and skin. May cause respiratory irritation. Some ethanols contain trace amounts of benzene or methanol, both of which are very toxic.
Care should be taken when working with these reagents. Avoid inhalation and contact with skin, eyes, and clothing. Goggles, gloves, and lab coats are required at all times.

Part I. Recovery of Salicylic Acid

1. Obtain an unknown mixture of sample as supplied by the laboratory instructor. Weigh the sample and record the weight on Data Sheet (your sample weight should be approximately 1.5g; if it is less than 1.35g or greater than 1.65g, obtain another sample). Add the mixture to a clean and dry, 100 or 150mL beaker.

2. Obtain 50mL of deionized water and add 10 drops of $3.0M$ H_2SO_4. Add the acidified water solution to the beaker. The acid will prevent any possible chemical reaction between the copper sulfate and the salicylic acid. Heat the mixture on a hot plate constantly stirring until all of the solid material has dissolved. **Avoid boiling the solution.** Remove the beaker from the heat, cover it with a watch glass and allow it to cool enough to be comfortable to the touch (**use caution when handling the hot beaker and solution).**

3. Place the beaker in an ice bath and allow salicylic acid to crystallize out of solution. A large quantity of salicylic acid needles should precipitate out of solution. Allow 10 minutes for complete precipitation of salicylic acid needles.

4. Set up a vacuum filtration apparatus as shown in Figure 13.3. Place a piece of pre-weighed filter paper in the Buchner funnel and start the aspirator.

5. Swirl the contents of the beaker and pour it into the Buchner funnel. Transfer the salicylic acid crystals as completely as possible to the funnel. Use no more than 10mL of cold deionized water to rinse the beaker to complete the transfer of the crystals. Allow the filtration to proceed for 10 minutes to initiate drying of the salicylic acid crystals. Press the funnel gently onto the flask to improve the vacuum.

6. **Remove the vacuum hose from the filtration flask before closing the faucet that controls the aspirator to prevent any water from being sucked into the flask.** Remove the Buchner funnel and transfer the blue solution into another clean, dry 150mL beaker.

7. Reassemble the filtration apparatus and draw air through the funnel for several minutes to remove as much water as possible from the salicylic acid crystals. Remove the filter paper with the salicylic acid crystals and place it on a watch glass to finish drying.

8. At the end of the lab period (about 2 hours), weigh the paper with the crystals. Record and calculate the mass of salicylic acid recovered.

Part II. Recovery of CuSO$_4$ · 5H$_2$O

1. Place the beaker with the copper sulfate solution (the filtrate) on the hot plate. Add a stirring rod and two boiling chips to the beaker and boil the solution *gently.* **Heating this solution without boiling chips could cause the solution to boil over violently.** Reduce the volume by boiling to about 20mL.

2. Obtain about 30mL of 95% ethanol while waiting for the copper sulfate solution to reduce. When the solution is reduced, carefully remove the beaker from the hot plate and using a spatula, remove the boiling chips from the solution.

3. While constantly stirring the solution, slowly add about 20mL of ethanol to cause the solution to become permanently cloudy. **Do not add the 95% ethanol until the copper sulfate solution is reduced to 20mL and after it is removed from the hot plate.** Cool the beaker to room temperature by letting it sit on the bench top and then further cool it in the ice bath to complete the precipitation of the crystals. Allow at least 10 minutes for complete precipitation.

4. Use the vacuum filtration apparatus and insert a pre-weighed filter paper in the Buchner funnel. Collect the crystals of CuSO$_4$ · 5H$_2$O as before. Use about 10mL of ethanol to transfer the crystals from the beaker to the funnel. Draw air through the funnel for 10 minutes to dry the crystals. The ethanol will evaporate and help to remove residual water.

5. Label a clean watch glass with your lab bench number with a permanent marker and obtain the mass of the labeled watch glass. Place the filter paper with the CuSO$_4$ · 5H$_2$O on the watch glass.

6. Place the watch glass and crystals in the oven at 90°C for at least 15 minutes to dry the sample prior to removing the water of hydration.

7. Remove the sample from the oven and allow to cool for several minutes. Weigh the watch glass and crystals.

8. On data sheet I, calculate and record the mass of CuSO$_4$· 5H$_2$O recovered. Add the mass of recovered salicylic acid to the mass of CuSO$_4$ · 5H$_2$O recovered. Calculate and record the total percent recovery based on the mass of the original sample. Calculate and record the percent by mass of each constituent in the recovered sample.

Part III. Removing the Water of Hydration

1. Place the watch glass with the CuSO$_4$ · 5H$_2$O crystals in the oven at 130°C for at least 15 minutes. The color of the crystals should change from blue to white with a bluish tint.

2. Remove the crystals from the oven and allow to cool for several minutes. Weigh the watch glass and crystals. Calculate and record the mass of the dehydrated crystals. Calculate how much water of hydration is left. Write the formula for the new hydrate.

DATA SHEET I

- Show a sample calculation for each type of calculated value.

Mass of unknown + filter paper   _____

Mass of filter paper   _____

Mass of unknown mixture   _____

SALICYLIC ACID CRYSTALLIZATION

Mass of salicylic acid + filter paper   _____

Mass of filter paper   _____

Mass of salicylic acid   _____

Calculation of percent salicylic acid in original mixture   _____

$CuSO_4 \cdot 5H_2O$ CRYSTALLIZATION

Mass of $CuSO_4 \cdot 5H_2O$ + filter paper + watch glass
(after drying at 90°C)   _____

Mass of watch glass   _____

Mass of filter paper   _____

Mass of $CuSO_4 \cdot 5H_2O$ _____

Calculation of percent $CuSO_4 \cdot 5H_2O$ in original mixture   _____

Percent of original sample not recovered   _____

DATA SHEET II

- Show a sample calculation for each type of calculated value.

REMOVAL OF WATER OF HYDRATION

Oven temperature for dehydration   _____

Actual time in oven   _____

Initial mass of $CuSO_4 \cdot 5H_2O$ _____

Final mass of $CuSO_4 \cdot XH_2O$ + filter paper + watch glass   _____

Final mass of $CuSO_4 \cdot XH_2O$ _____

Mass of water removed   _____

Calculation of **X** in $CuSO_4 \cdot \mathbf{X}H_2O$ _____

Post-Laboratory Questions

1. Discuss the problems that were encountered in conducting the experiment:
   a. In the recovery of salicylic acid:
      1. What could have accounted for any losses (one reason)?

      2. What could have caused an incorrectly high calculation of salicylic acid (*one reason*)?

   b. In the recovery of $CuSO_4 \cdot 5H_2O$:
      1. What could have accounted for any losses (one reason)?

      2. What could have an incorrectly high calculation of $CuSO_4 \cdot 5H_2O$ (one reason)?

2. A 1.250g sample of $BaCl_2 \cdot xH_2O$ has a mass of 1.060g after heating. Assuming all of the water of crystallization was lost by heating, find the experimental value of x.

BEFORE YOU COME TO LAB YOU MUST COMPLETE A PRELAB ASSIGNMENT:

Experiment 13: Separation by Fractional Crystallization Online PRELAB Quiz:

- The Separation by Fractional Crystallization Online PRELAB Quiz is composed of multiple choice questions.
- The PRELAB score accounts for 40 points of your total lab score.
- The PRELAB quiz is timed, and it must be submitted before **11:59pm the night before your experiment.**
- You may only submit the PRELAB quiz once.
- In order to prepare for your PRELAB quiz, it is recommended that you study the background information, calculations, and lab procedure for the experiment in your lab manual. You may be asked to perform calculations; the correct answer will need to be reported to the proper number of significant figures and with the appropriate units.
- You may be asked to prepare and print out a graph that you will turn into your instructors when you come to lab.

14

Graphical Analysis

BACKGROUND

In the experimental sciences, data is often collected in pairs. The data pairs consist of an independent and a dependent variable. The independent variable value is set by the experiment design while the dependent variable value is measured and is a function of the independent variable. The relationship between the two variables can be visually expressed and analyzed graphically in the x-y plane. The x-axis (also called the abscissa) is always used for the independent variable; the y-axis (also called the ordinate) is used for the dependent variable.

Gas laws provide several good examples of linear relationships with a characteristic equation, $y = mx + b$, where x is the independent variable, y is the dependent variable, m is the slope, and b is the y-intercept.

Avogadro's Law gives us the relationship between the volume (V) of an ideal gas as a function of the number of moles (n). The data set and Logger Pro© graph are shown in Figure 14.1.

n(mols)	V(L)
0.1	2.45
0.2	4.89
0.3	7.34
0.4	9.78
0.5	12.23

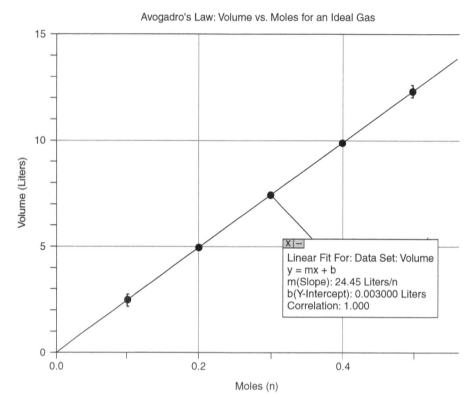

Figure 14.1 Linear Relationship; Volume vs. Moles

Another interesting illustration is possible with Boyle's Law, where we see an inverse relationship between volume (V) and pressure (P). The data set and Logger Pro© graph are shown in Figure 14.2.

P(atm)	V(L)
1	2.45
5	0.489
10	0.245
50	0.0489
100	0.0245
200	0.0122
500	0.00489
1000	0.00245

In this take-home experiment designed by Vernier, you will study various functional relationships between two variables and different ways to graphically represent them.

EXAMPLE 1

Suppose you have these four ordered pairs, and you want to determine the relationship between *x* and *y*:

x	y
2	6
3	9
5	15
9	27

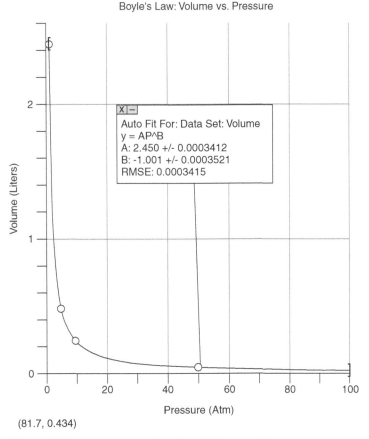

Figure 14.2 Inverse Relationship; Volume vs. Pressure

The first logical step is to make a graph of *y* versus *x*.

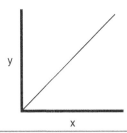

Because the shape of the plot is a straight line that passes through the origin (0,0), it is a simple *direct* relationship. An equation is written showing this relationship: $y = k \cdot x$. This is done by writing the variable from the vertical axis (dependent variable) on the left side of the equation, and then equating it to a proportionality constant, *k*, multiplied by *x*, the independent variable. The constant, *k*, can be determined either by finding the slope of the graph or by solving your equation for *k* ($k = y/x$), and finding *k* for one of your ordered pairs. In this simple example, $k = 6/2 = 3$. If it is the correct proportionality constant, then you should get the same *k* value by dividing any of the *y* values by the corresponding *x* value. The equation can now be written:

$$y = 3 \cdot x \qquad (y \text{ varies directly with } x)$$

EXAMPLE 2

Consider these ordered pairs:

x	y
1	2
2	8
3	18
4	32

First plot y versus x. The graph looks like this:

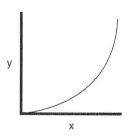

Because this graph is not a straight line passing through the origin, you must make another graph. It appears that y increases as x increases. However, the increase is not proportional (direct). Rather, y varies *exponentially* with x. Thus y might vary with the *square* of x or the *cube* of x. The next logical plot would be y versus x^2. The graph looks like this:

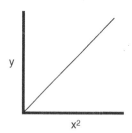

Since this plot is a straight line passing through the origin, y varies with the square of x, and the equation is:

$$y = k \cdot x^2$$

Again, place y on one side of the equation and x^2 on the other, multiplying x^2 by the proportionality constant, k. Determine k by dividing y by x^2:

$$k = y/x^2 = 8/(2)^2 = 8/4 = 2$$

This value will be the same for any of the four ordered pairs, and yields the equation:

$$y = 2 \cdot x^2 \qquad (y \text{ varies directly with the square of } x)$$

EXAMPLE 3

x	y
2	24
3	16
4	12
8	6
12	4

A plot of *y* versus *x* gives a graph that looks like this:

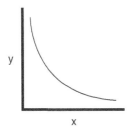

A graph with this curve always suggests an inverse relationship. To confirm an inverse relationship, plot the reciprocal of one variable versus the other variable. In this case, *y* is plotted versus the reciprocal of *x*, or 1/*x*. The graph looks like this:

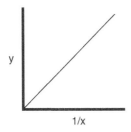

Because this graph yields a straight line that passes through the origin (0,0), the relationship between *x* and *y* is inverse. Using the same method we used in examples 1 and 2, the equation would be:

$y = k(1/x)$ or $y = k/x$

To find the constant, solve for *k* ($k = y \cdot x$). Using any of the ordered pairs, determine *k*:

$k = 2 \times 24 = 48$

Thus the equation would be:

$y = 48/x$ (*y* varies inversely with *x*)

EXAMPLE 4

The fourth and final example has the following ordered pairs:

x	y
1.0	48.00
1.5	14.20
2.0	6.00
3.0	1.78
4.0	0.75

A plot of *y* versus *x* looks like this:

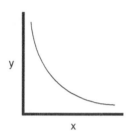

Thus the relationship must be inverse. Now plot *y* versus the reciprocal of *x*. The plot of *y* versus 1/*x* looks like this:

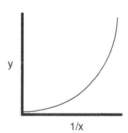

Because this graph is not a straight line, the relationship is not just inverse, but rather inverse square or inverse cube.

The next logical step is to plot *y* versus $1/x^2$ (inverse square). The plot of this graph is shown below. The line still is not straight, so the relationship is not inverse square.

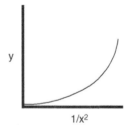

Finally, try a plot of y versus $1/x^3$. Aha! This plot comes out to be a straight line passing through the origin.

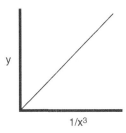

This must be the correct relationship. The equation for the relationship is:

$$y = k(1/x^3) \text{ or } y = k/x^3$$

Now, determine a value for the constant, k. For example, $k = y \cdot x^3 = (6)(2)^3 = 48$. Check to see if it is constant for other ordered pairs. The equation for this relationship is:

$$y = 48/x^3 \quad (y \text{ varies inversely with the cube of } x)$$

PROCEDURE

1. Each student will do 6 problems to be assigned by your instructor from the 30-problem list given. Print out six Logger Pro© graphs and complete the required data sheets and tables. Please refer to the Graphical Analysis Selection Criteria on the last page of this experiment to select your problem set.

2. Begin by opening the file "05 Find the Relationship" from the *Chemistry with Vernier* folder of Logger Pro©. Choose to continue without the interface.

3. Enter the data pairs in the table.
   a. Click on the first cell in the x column in the table. Type in the x value for the first data pair, and press the **Enter** key.
   b. The cursor will now be in the first cell in the y column. Type in the y value for the first data pair, and press the **Enter** key.
   c. Continue in this manner to enter the remaining data pairs.

4. Examine the shape of the curve in the graph. If the graph is curved (varies inversely or exponentially), proceed as described in the introduction of this experiment. To do this using Logger Pro©, it is necessary to create a new column of data, x^n, where x represents the original x column in the Table window, and n is the value of the exponent:
   a. Choose **New Calculated Column** from the **Data** menu.
   b. Enter a **Name** that corresponds to the formula you will enter (e.g., "x^2", "x^{-1}"). Use an exponent of "2" or "3" for a power that increases exponentially, "–1" for the reciprocal of n, "–2" for inverse square, or "–3" for inverse cube. Leave the **Short Name** and **Unit** boxes empty.
   c. Enter the correct formula for the column (x^n) in the **Equation** edit box. To do this, select "x" from the **Variables** list. Following "x" in the **Equation** edit box, type in "^", then type in the value for the exponent, n, that you used in the previous step. Click. According to the exponent of n you entered, a corresponding set of calculated values will appear in a modified column in the table.
   d. Click on the horizontal-axis label, select "x^n". You should now see a graph of y versus x^n. To autoscale both axes starting with zero, double-click in the center of the graph to view Graph Options, click the **Axis Options** tab, and select **Autoscale from 0** from the scaling menu for both axes. Click.

5. To see if you made the correct choice of exponents:

    a. If a straight line results, you have made the correct choice—proceed to step 6. If it is still curved, double-click on the calculated column, x^n, heading. Decide on a new value for *n,* then edit the value of *n* that you originally entered (in the x^n formula in the **Equation** edit box). Change the exponent in the **Name.** Click

        Done .

    b. A new set of values for this power of *x* will appear in the modified column; these values will automatically be plotted on the graph.

    c. You should now see a graph of *y* vs. x^n. If necessary, autoscale both axes starting from zero.

    d. If the points are in a straight line, proceed to step 6. If not, repeat the step-5 procedure until a straight line is obtained.

6. After you have obtained a straight line, click the **Linear Fit** button, ⟋. The regression line is calculated by the computer as a best-fit straight line passing through or near the data points, and will be shown on the graph.

7. Since you will need to use the original data pairs in processing the data, record the *x* and *y* values, the value of *n* used in your final linear graph, and the problem number in the **Data and Calculations** table.

8. To print your linear graph of *y* vs. x^n:

    a. Label the curves by choosing **Text Annotation** from the **Insert** menu, and typing the number of the problem you just solved in the edit box (e.g., *Problem 23*). Drag the box to a position near the curve. Adjust the position of the arrowhead by clicking and dragging it.

    b. **Title** your graph "y vs. x^n" using the appropriate n value.

    c. **Print** a copy of the graph. Make sure your name, the date, your section, and lab locker # appear in the print footer.

9. To confirm that you made the right choice for the exponent, *n,* you can use a second method. Instead of a *linear* regression plot of *y* vs. x^n, you can create a *power* regression curve on the original plot of *y* vs. *x*. Using the method described below, you can also calculate a value for *a* and *n* in the equation, *y* = A · x^n.

    a. To return to the original plot of *y* vs. *x,* click on the horizontal-axis label, and select "x". Remove the linear regression and annotation floating boxes.

    b. Click the **Curve Fit** button Try Fit .

                        c.   Choose your mathematical relationship from the list at the lower left: **Use Variable Power** (y = Ax^n). To confirm that the exponent, *n,* is the same as the value you recorded earlier, enter the value of *n* in the **Power** edit box at the bottom. Click the Try Fit button.

    d. A best-fit curve will be displayed on the graph. The curve should match up well with the points if you made the correct choice. If the curve does not match up well, try a different power and click Try Fit again. When the curve has a good fit with the data points, then click

        OK .

10. To do another problem, reopen "05 Find the Relationship." **Important:** Click on the **No** button when asked if you want to save the changes to the previous problem. -Repeat steps 3–9 for the new problem.

Processing the Data

1. Using x, y, and k, write an equation that represents the relationship between y and x for each problem. Use the value for n that you determined from the graphing exercise. Write your final answer using only positive exponents. For example, if $y = k \cdot x^{-2}$, then rewrite the answer as: $y = k / x^2$. See the Data and Calculations table for examples.

2. Solve each equation for k. Then calculate the numerical value of k. Do this for at least two ordered pairs, as shown in the example, to confirm that k is really constant.

3. Rewrite the equation, using x, y, and the *numerical value* of k.

4. You will turn in the six graphs associated with your six assigned problems and the data sheets.

DATA AND CALCULATIONS TABLE

Problem Number _____	
X	Y
n =	

Problem Number _____	
X	Y
n =	

Problem Number _____	
X	Y
n =	

Problem Number _____	
X	Y
n =	

Problem Number _____	
X	Y
n =	

Problem Number _____	
X	Y
n =	

Problem Number	Equation (using *x*, *y*, & *k*)	Solve for "*k*" (find the value of *k* for two data pairs)	Final Equation (*x*, *y* and value of *k*)

PROBLEM SET

1.			7.			13.			19.			25.		
	x	y		x	y		x	y		x	y		x	y
	0.60	.198		0.20	.290		1.5	1.13		45	405		89	8.72
	0.80	.264		0.25	.363		2.0	1.50		37	333		321	31.5
	1.5	.495		0.30	.435		2.5	1.88		16	144		47	4.61
	2.0	.660		0.45	.653		3.5	2.63		4.0	36		213	20.9
	2.5	.825		0.60	.870		5.0	3.75		64	576		436	42.7

2.			8.			14.			20.			26.		
	x	y		x	y		x	y		x	y		x	y
	32	819		0.7	16.7		2.0	8.0		4.0	8.0		0.10	.0020
	13	135		1.2	49.0		8.0	128		3.0	4.5		0.20	.0080
	43	1479		1.8	110		6.0	72		7.0	24.5		0.30	.018
	8	51.2		4.5	689		5.0	50.0		5.0	12.5		0.50	.050
	24	461		2.5	213		3.0	18		8.0	32.0		0.70	.098

3.			9.			15.			21.			27.		
	x	y		x	y		x	y		x	y		x	y
	1.0	2.0		0.400	.192		0.100	.000500		7.00	82.3		0.50	2.25
	2.0	16		0.600	.648		0.500	.06250		12.0	415		0.80	9.22
	3.0	54		0.200	.024		0.300	.01350		10.0	240		1.10	24.0
	4.0	128		0.800	1.54		0.700	.17150		15.0	810		1.90	123.5
	5.0	250		0.900	2.19		1.000	.50000		3.0	6.48		0.20	0.144

4.			10.			16.			22.			28.		
	x	y		x	y		x	y		x	y		x	y
	2.00	1.50		2.500	10.00		6.00	2.50		14	5.36		5.0	0.16
	2.50	1.20		1.500	16.67		9.00	1.67		25	3.00		2.0	0.40
	1.50	2.00		12.00	2.083		10.0	1.50		19	3.95		8.0	0.10
	3.00	1.00		19.00	1.316		12.0	1.25		36	2.08		15.0	0.053
	5.00	0.60		5.000	5.000		20.0	0.75		48	1.56		0.50	1.60

5.			11.			17.			23.			29.		
	x	y		x	y		x	y		x	y		x	y
	2.00	1.00		5.0	0.84		1.5	5.33		5.0	5.80		0.500	3.000
	3.00	0.444		2.0	5.25		2.0	3.00		11.0	1.20		0.800	1.170
	5.00	0.160		3.0	2.33		5.0	0.48		15.0	0.644		1.30	0.444
	1.50	1.78		4.8	0.91		3.8	0.83		24.0	0.252		2.00	0.188
	8.00	.0625		7.5	0.373		6.0	0.333		30.0	0.161		3.00	.0833

6.			12.			18.			24.			30.		
	x	y		x	y		x	y		x	y		x	y
	11	0.236		0.85	1.04		0.40	78.1		4.5	.154		2.00	3.00
	17	.0639		1.50	.190		0.90	6.85		5.0	.112		3.00	0.889
	6.0	1.454		0.50	5.12		0.70	14.6		7.0	.041		5.00	0.192
	28.0	.0143		2.00	.080		1.2	2.89		3.0	.519		7.00	0.070
	20.0	.0393		3.00	.0237		0.60	23.2		8.0	.0273		9.00	0.033

EXPERIMENT 14: GRAPHICAL ANALYSIS

The following table represents the 30 problems from which you are to select 6 problems (one from each row) using the rules below:

	Column A	Column B	Column C	Column D	Column E
Row 1	1	7	13	19	25
Row 2	2	8	14	20	26
Row 3	3	9	15	21	27
Row 4	4	10	16	22	28
Row 5	5	11	17	23	29
Row 6	6	12	18	24	30

Rules:

You will select one problem from each row;

For row 1:
Select from column   A   if your birthday is in   Jan, Feb, Mar
   B   Apr, May, Jun
   C   Jul, Aug
   D   Sep, Oct
   E   Nov, Dec

For row 2:
Select from column   A   if your locker # is   1-9
   B   10-19
   C   20-29
   D   30-39
   E   40-50

For row 3:
Select from column   A   if your locker # ends with   0 or 5
   B   1 or 6
   C   2 or 7
   D   3 or 8
   E   4 or 9

For row 4:
Select from column   A   if your first name begins with   a-e
   B   f-i
   C   j-o
   D   p-r
   E   s-z

For row 5:

Select from column	A	if your first name ends with	a-e
	B		f-i
	C		j-o
	D		p-r
	E		s-z

For row 6:

Select from column	A	if your last name ends with	a-e
	B		f-i
	C		j-o
	D		p-r
	E		s-z

Working with Numbers in the Chemistry Lab

A. Precision and accuracy

Precision is the measure of how close or reproducible a series of experimental measurements are to each other. **Accuracy** is how close any measurement is to the actual value.

B. Error analysis

Systematic error is one which is consistently higher or lower than the actual value. It is the result of either a faulty measuring devise or consistently making the incorrect reading.

Random error can be either higher or lower than the actual value. This type of error always occurs and is the result of operator skill and instrument precision.

The **mean** ($\bar{x}$) is the average of a series of measurements.

The **range** of a set of measurements is the difference between the largest and smallest values.

The **standard deviation** (S) of a set of measurements is a measure of how far apart the individual measurements are from the mean.

$$\sigma = \sqrt{\frac{1}{(n-1)}\sum_{1}^{n}(\bar{x}-x_i)^2}$$

C. Significant figures by John Halpin

The CHEM-UA 125/CHEM-UA 126 Policy on Significant Figures

If I give you a numerical value, but you have no idea how precise it is, then the information is useless to you. We have to have a prior agreement (perhaps an implicit one) that allows you to know how much you can "*trust*" my information. When using the English language (or any other spoken language), we have ways of indicating precision. If I tell you that I'm "about 29 years old" (Ha!), then you know it's approximate. If I tell you that I am "78 years, 3 months, 2 days, 8 hours, 47 minutes, and 32 seconds old", that is less approximate (and more precise). Neither age is accurate, by the way. Unfortunately, when simply reporting a numerical quantity (with its unit, of course!) there are no cues concerning precision. "29 years" might mean anything from 28.50000000000000000001 years to 29.49999999999999999999 years. You wouldn't know what "29 years" means without further information. Similarly, if I didn't know the time of day of my birth, then I would have no right (i.e., I'd be lying) to say that I am "78 years, 3 months, 2 days, 8 hours, 47 minutes, and 32 seconds old". In this course, you and I will trade a lot of numerical data. We had better discuss how to interpret this information so that we can communicate.

What we will do is agree to report measured data in the following fashion: report all digits that you are sure about, plus one more digit that you have estimated. For example, if you tell me that you are 170.18 cm tall, I will understand that to mean that you have measured your height and your measurement device *convinced* you that you are between 170.1 cm and 170.2 cm (the device must have been clearly marked off to the tenth of a cm). Further, it looks to you as though you are considerably closer to 170.2 cm, so that you estimate that you are 0.08 cm taller than 170.1 cm (i.e., you believe that you are 170.18 cm tall). To give me fewer digits would mean that you are "holding back" information that you *do* have. To give me more digits would be lying (or, at least, an exaggeration). Our agreement on how many digits should be reported allows you to send information about precision along with your numerical value **and** it allows me to receive that information.

Now if I use your information in a calculation, I have to regard my result as being limited in *its* precision by the data (your data) upon which it is based. That way, if I pass my result on to someone else (or even back to you) the recipient gets the appropriate precision information. Therefore, we have to establish another agreement about how to determine the appropriate number of significant figures to include in a calculated result. You will find our agreement (I am confident that you *will* agree!) below.

What you will find below is simply a set of time saving rules. By obeying these rules, your answers to my questions will agree (in terms of precision) with my answers to my questions. These are not the only rules that exist, nor are they the "best". Some sets of rules do a better job than others. By that, I mean that "better" ones more closely duplicate the results of a complete and laborious error analysis. The most accurate sets of rules tend to be difficult to use. When they are used, there seem to be many "borderline" cases where more than one rule *might* apply. Since we are using the rules to save time, so that we can devote more attention to other important matters (such as chemistry), I have adopted a particularly simple procedure for the General Chemistry courses. It is not the best, but it's not too bad. It has so few ambiguities that we can expect every student in the class to be able to arrive at the same answer (provided that they don't make a mistake). At the same time, I point out and hope that students note, that these simple rules are APPROXIMATE and that if they ever do a calculation for which the precision of the result is of great importance, then they should NOT use the rules, but should sit down and do a careful data analysis. If lives will depend upon your results (e.g., you design bridges for a living) please don't use my rules after you've completed General Chemistry I and II!!!

The procedure for General Chemistry:

If you solve a problem that involves ONLY addition and/or subtraction (well, possibly mult/div by a number of "counted objects" or by "defined quantities", neither of which is considered to be subject to the "random" error of measurements), then use the ADDITION/SUBTRACTION RULE.

THE ADDITION/SUBTRACTION RULE: round your answer off to the same DECIMAL PLACE as the least precise piece of data that was involved in the calculation (including conversion factors that depend upon measurements rather than definitions and those that have been rounded off, e.g., 1 mile 1.6×10^3 m).

If you solve a problem that involves ONLY multiplication and/or division, use then use the MULTIPLICATION/DIVISION RULE.

THE MULTIPLICATION/DIVISION RULE: round your answer until it contains the SAME NUMBER OF SIGNIFICANT DIGITS as the least precise piece of data that was involved in the calculation (again, including "measured" conversion factors), regardless of the position of the decimal point.

If you solve a problem that involves both addition (or subtraction) AND multiplication (or division), use the *multiplication/division rule*, **EXCEPT** every time you perform a subtraction, assess how many sig figs would be used in its answer (via the addition/subtraction rule) and then regard that subtractive result as an item of data (i.e., subtractions might lower the number of sig figs in the overall answer).

ONLY ROUND OFF WHEN REPORTING AN ANSWER. If you know (from looking at the data) that you'll eventually be rounding the answer off to a particular number of significant figures (or to a particular decimal place) then keep AT LEAST TWO (2) EXTRA DIGITS (preferably more) throughout your calculation in order to avoid contributing "round off" error to the result.

If you need to use a reported result for further calculation, use its value from "before rounding".

Now, if you disagree with these rules, that's fine. They're not perfect. This procedure does not duplicate the outcome of a careful error analysis 100% of the time. But it does a pretty good job and involves little ambiguity. For a course of nearly 700 students, it's workable. If I taught bridge design, we wouldn't use it. However, in order to draw SOME ATTENTION to questions of precision, without going overboard with issues of applied mathematics, the procedure described above is a good compromise.

General Chemistry students (at NYU) must use it.
For other courses, do what the instructor says.
For bridge design, do it the *right* way!

D. Scientific notation

Scientific notation is a system to represent numbers, no matter how large or small, in a consistent and concise format. The system is unambiguous with regard to significant figures and so many misunderstandings can be avoided by using scientific notation. Any number can be represented as some other number times a factor of 10. For example, the number 896735421 can be represented in scientific notation as 8.96735421×10^8. Or the number 0.00000000000045738929 can be written as $4.5738929 \times 10^{-14}$. Notice in each case the number we use to multiply by the factor of 10 is between 1 and 10 by convention.

Since we do not sacrifice accuracy in using scientific notation while eliminating the ambiguity of numbers written without a decimal point, it is recommended that scientific notation should be used whenever practical. The rules of mathematical operations using scientific notation are consistent with those rules presented above.

E. Logarithms

A logarithm is an exponent. For example, $\log_{10}100 = 2$ is the same as $10^2 = 100$. Log_{10} is stated as log to the base 10 and is called the common logarithm. Usually the subscript 10 is left off and we understand that log means base 10 logarithm. A system of logarithms can be developed for any "base"; however, logs to the base 10 and logs to the base e, where $e = 2.71828\ldots$ are used commonly where log to the base e is abbreviated ln and is called the natural log. The natural log is related to the common log as follows: $\ln b = 2.303 \log b$.

$\log 1 = 0$	$10^0 = 1$	$\log 1 = 0$	$10^0 = 1$
$\log 10 = 1$	$10^1 = 10$	$\log 10^{-1} = -1$	$10^{-1} = .1$
$\log 10^2 = 2$	$10^2 = 100$	$\log 10^{-2} = -2$	$10^{-2} = .01$
$\log 10^3 = 3$	$10^3 = 1000$	$\log 10^{-3} = -3$	$10^{-3} = .001$
$\log 10^4 = 4$	$10^4 = 10000$	$\log 10^{-4} = -4$	$10^{-4} = .0001$
$\log 10^5 = 5$	$10^5 = 100000$	$\log 10^{-5} = -5$	$10^{-5} = .00001$
$\log 10^6 = 6$	$10^6 = 1000000$	$\log 10^{-6} = -6$	$10^{-6} = .000001$
$\log 10^7 = 7$	$10^7 = 10000000$	$\log 10^{-7} = -7$	$10^{-7} = .0000001$
$\log 10^8 = 8$	$10^8 = 100000000$	$\log 10^{-8} = -8$	$10^{-8} = .00000001$
$\log 10^9 = 9$	$10^9 = 1000000000$	$\log 10^{-9} = -9$	$10^{-9} = .000000001$
$\log 10^{10} = 10$	$10^{10} = 10000000000$	$\log 10^{-10} = -10$	$10^{-10} = .0000000001$

While in these examples, logarithms can be obtained by inspection, this is not possible with most numbers such as 2578.95. In this case we can use any scientific calculator to get the log. We'll see that the log 2578.95 = 3.411442922. To properly represent the number, we must be consistent with significant figures. The number 2578.95 has 6 significant figures and so the log should have the same number of significant figures. The number to the left of the decimal, 3 in this case, is *not* significant since it only tells us the magnitude of the number. The proper representation would be 3.411442 which has 6 digits to the right of the decimal which are significant.

We will use logarithms when making pH calculations. The definition of pH is as follows:

$$pH = -\log [H^+] \text{ or } pH = -\log[H_3O^+]$$

where $[H^+]$ is the molar concentration of the hydrogen ion and $[H_3O^+]$ is the molar concentration of the hydronium ion. We must be able to calculate pH from $[H^+]$ or $[H_3O^+]$ and also compute $[H^+]$ and $[H_3O^+]$ from pH. This 2nd calculation requires the use of the antilog function which is the inverse of the log function. Both calculations should be mastered by the student.

F. Reporting Data on your data sheet:

Data must be reported with proper units and significant figures. In addition, sample calculations must be provided. It is good form to record the type of equipment used for each measurement.

Sample calculations must be shown for each new type of calculation performed. Your sample calculations should show numbers to all experimental accuracy, rounding only your answer to significant figures.

SAMPLE DATA SHEET

SHOW A SAMPLE CALCULATION FOR EACH TYPE OF CALCULATED VALUE.

- Density of a Rubber Stopper

Trial #	*1*	*2*	*3*
Mass of rubber stopper *(g)*	9.24	9.23	9.24
(top-loading balance)			
Initial volume of water *(mL)*	22.3	25.6	18.7
(50mL grad. cyl.)			
Final volume with stopper *(mL)*	30.6	34.1	27.2
Volume of stopper *(mL)*	8.3	8.5	8.5

S.C.: 30.6mL – 22.3mL = 8.3mL

Density of stopper *(g/mL)*	1.1	1.1	1.1
	(1.113253012)	*(1.085882353)*	*(1.087058824)*

Mean value _____ *1.1 g/mL* _____

Standard deviation _____ *0.028 g/mL* _____

Density of Stopper S.C.: 9.24g/8.3mL = 1.113253012g/mL = 1.1mL

Mean Value S.C: (1.1132503102g/mL + 1.085882353g/mL + 1.087058824g/mL) / 3

$$= 1.095398063g/mL = 1.1g/mL$$

Standard deviation S.C: $\bar{x} = 1.0953980630$

$$S = \sqrt{\frac{(\bar{x}-1.1132503012)^2+(\bar{x}-1.085882353)^2+(\bar{x}-1.087058824)^2}{3-1}}$$

$$= .0277387933 = .028\,g/ml$$

APPENDIX II

Lab Equipment

Utility Clamp

Cork

Utility Clamp Holder

Screw Clamp

Ring

Bunsen Burner

Rubber Pipette bulb

Wash Bottle

Rubber Stopper

Watch Glass

Wire Mesh

Test Tube Brush

Tongs

Funnel

Erlenmeyer Flask

500ml
5%

500 ml
PYREX
USA

400

300

200

100

Filter Flask

250ml
5%

250 ml
PYREX
USA

200

150

100

50

Beaker

Buret Clamp

Test Tubes

Test Tube Holder

Medicine dropper (or transfer pipet)

Büchner funnel

Mortar and pestle

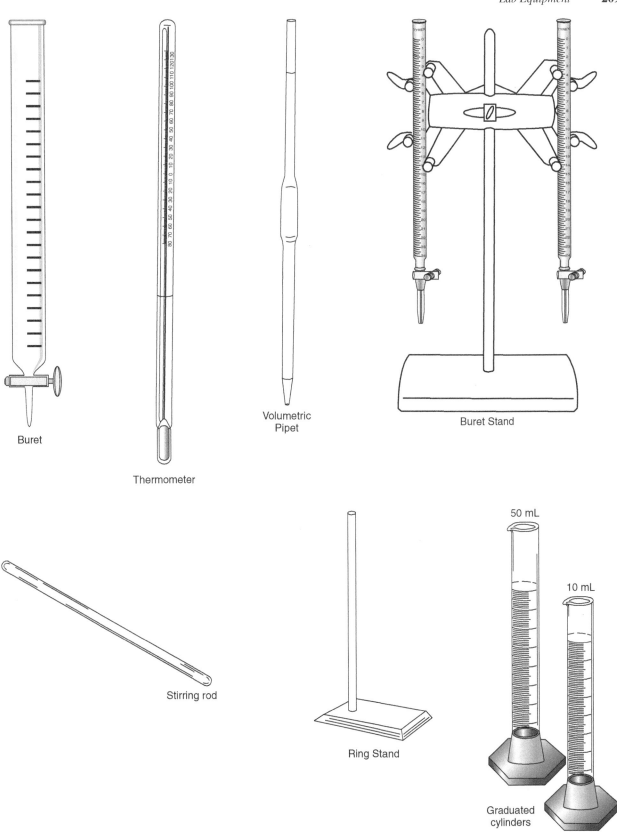

Buret

Thermometer

Volumetric
Pipet

Buret Stand

Stirring rod

Ring Stand

50 mL

10 mL

Graduated
cylinders

Analytical Balance

Top Loading Balance

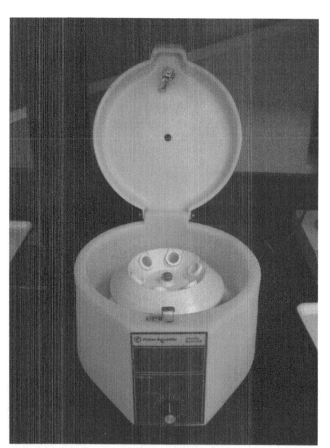

Lab Centrifuge

Pipet Pump

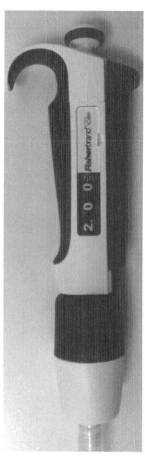

Automatic Pipet

Introduction to Basic Laboratory Equipment and Methods

GRAVIMETRIC MEASUREMENTS

Laboratory balances should be regularly serviced including leveling and calibration. It is essential that balances are kept clean. For consistent measurements, the same balance should be used throughout an experiement when possible.

Analytical Balance: (see illustration in Appendix II)

Modern electronic analytical balances used in the chemistry laboratory have a total capacity of 100–200 g. Typical precision of these balances is 0.0001 g. Analytical balances are built within a glass enclosure to minimize the effect of air movement. When weighing a solid or liquid reagent, use a weighing boat or beaker. To begin, you calibrate the balance or initialize it by setting it to zero just prior to your weighing. Some balances have the provision to set the zero with the weighing boat on the platform, effectively subtracting the weight of the vessel from the total weight. This is called taring. Then add your reagent slowly until you have the required amount. If taring is not permitted, weigh the empty vessel, and then weigh it again after adding the reagent. Determine the reagent weight by subtracting the weight of the empty vessel from the weight of the vessel and reagent.

Top Loading Balance: (see illustration in Appendix II)

The capacity of the top loading balance is larger while its precision is lower. The higher the capacity of the balance, the lower is the precision. Minimally, the precision should be 0.01 g. There is no glass enclosure to minimize air movements and, as a result, high precision is not possible. The method of weighing with the top loading balance is the same as with the analytical balance. Taring may or may not be available. If not, weigh by difference as described above.

VOLUMETRIC MEASUREMENT OF LIQUIDS

Glassware Types and Cleaning

The types of glassware that we will use include: beakers, flasks (Erlenmeyer or filter), test tubes, graduated cylinders, pipets, burets, and volumetric flasks. Laboratory glassware should always be cleaned and dried whenever possible to avoid contamination. Clean with an approved laboratory glassware cleaner, rinse with tap water, and then do a final rinse with deionized water. To avoid pouring chemically contaminated water down the sink, your first two rinses should be disposed of as hazardous waste.

In this course you will use three types of precision calibrated glassware: burets, pipets and flasks. This type of calibrated glassware is usually referred to as <u>volumetric glassware</u>. This precision glassware is capable of measurements of volume that are good

Figure III.2
Graduated
cylinder

to four significant digits and is consequently expensive. You should be careful in handling this type of equipment so that breakage losses are minimized.

Do not use soap when cleaning volumetric glassware, as it tends to contaminate the glassware. Do rinse very thoroughly as above both before and immediately after use.

When making volumetric measurements, you will usually wet the surfaces of the glassware to be used with the liquid being measured. This initial liquid will be discarded as waste and the glassware refilled to a specific volume.

Graduated Cylinders

A graduated cylinder (Figure III.2) is used to measure approximate volumes of a liquid. These cylinders come in many sizes, but commonly we will use 10 mL, 50 mL and 100 mL sizes in our experiments. The size of the cylinder will determine the precision of your measurements- a smaller cylinder will provide more accuracy.

When measuring the volume of an aqueous solution (a solution with water as the solvent) or pure water in a graduated cylinder, the surface of the liquid will be concave due to surface tension forces acting between the glass and the liquid. To best read your volumes of aqueous solutions, or any liquid that forms a concave surface, read the bottom of the curvature, called the *meniscus*. If you were measuring the volume of liquid mercury, the liquid metal surface would be convex because mercury does not "wet" glass. In the case of a liquid that forms a convex surface you would read the top of the meniscus.

Your readings should always be taken at eye level to avoid parallax error (the apparent displacement of an object as seen from two different points that are not on a line with the object). See Figure III.3.

To read a graduated cylinder (or any graduated instrument in the lab) to the proper precision, report the data to the nearest calibration mark and add an estimated digit. For example, if the bottom of a meniscus in a graduated cylinder lies approximately halfway between 1.7 and 1.8 mLs, we would approximate the last digit and report the volume as 1.75 mL.

Pipets

The two main types of pipets are transfer and measuring pipets. A volumetric pipet is a type of transfer pipet calibrated to deliver only one volume (see Figure III.4). These pipets come in many sizes but common ones are 5 mL, 10 mL, 25 mL and 50 mL. Measuring pipets are graduated so you can deliver any volume (usually to the nearest tenth of a milliliter). Measuring pipets are available in 1 mL, 5 mL, and 10 mL sizes.

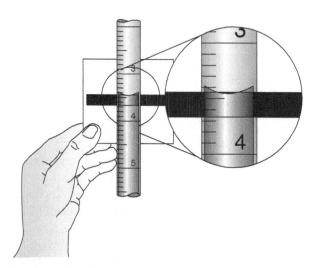

Figure III.3   The meniscus

measuring
pipet

volumetric
pipet

Figure III.4   Pipets

The use of a pipet requires learning a technique using a rubber to suck the liquid into the pipet. Never try to fill a pipet by sucking with your mouth. First clean and rinse your pipet as described above. The steps are illustrated in Figure III.5(a–e).

a) Compress the rubber bulb and place it carefully over the upper end of the pipet. The bulb only needs to cover the end of the pipet to create an airtight seal, there is no need to push the pipet further into the bulb. You may want to lubricate the bulb hole with a drop of deionized water.

b) Place the tip of the pipet in the liquid and draw the liquid in to above the calibration line. Keep the pipet tip submerged to avoid air bubble entry.

Be careful not to draw the liquid into the bulb. Dispose of this first amount of liquid in a waste beaker.

c) Draw in the liquid to be measured above the calibration line. Remove the bulb while simultaneously covering the tip with your index finger (this process requires considerable skill to develop and no one is born innately able to do this; you will learn with practice).

Now allow the liquid level to drop to the required level by slowly allowing air to enter the pipet by controlled lifting of your finger.

d) When the liquid level is at the correct place, move the pipet tip to the glassware where you want the liquid delivered and release your finger.

Allow the pipet to drain into the container and touch off any last drop on the pipet on the side of the glassware.

e) There may be some liquid remaining in the pipet tip. Do not blow this remaining liquid from the pipet. The pipet was calibrated to deliver the correct volume with this liquid remaining.

This method works fine for both types of pipets.

Alternatively, a pipet pump can be used (Figure III.6). A pipet pump is color-coded, orange for 25 mL size pipets, green for 10 mL pipets or smaller.

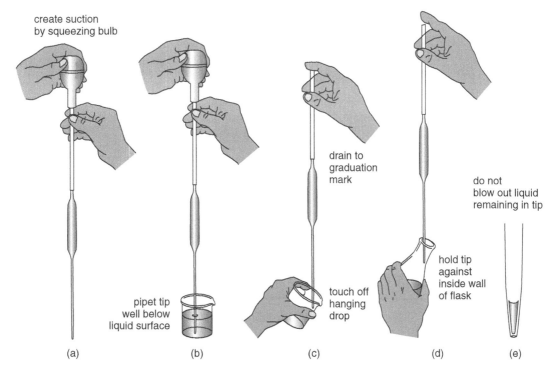

Figure III.5   Filling procedure

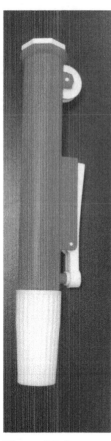

Figure III.6
Pipet pump

a) First, unscrew the white collar a few revolutions, then insert the end of the pipet into the pipet pump. Unscrewing the collar will allow the pipet to enter the pump with less pressure.

b) After the pipet is inserted, twist the white collar in the opposite direction in order to tighten it and create an air-tight seal. Without an air-tight seal, the liquid level in the pipet will drop as soon as it's drawn up the pipet. Push the plunger on the pipet pump all the way down.

c) To draw liquid into the pipet, simply roll the thumbwheel to draw up liquid. Draw liquid above the calibration mark. Discard this liquid into your waste beaker as a rinse. In order to dispense the liquid, press the quick-release button on the side of the pipet pump to dispense the solution. Repeat this process once more.

d) Now draw liquid into the pipet until slightly above the calibration mark. When you withdraw the pipet from the solution, the liquid in the pipet will drop slightly. You may need to draw more solution into the pipet to adjust for this.

e) When the liquid level is in the correct place, move the pipet tip to the glassware where you want the liquid to be delivered. Hold down the quick-release button to dispense the liquid. Touch the pipet to the side of the container to touch off any drops of liquid hanging off the pipet.

f) There may be some liquid remaining in the pipet tip. Do not blow this remaining liquid from the pipet. The pipet was calibrated to deliver the correct volume with this liquid remaining.

Automatic Pipet

Using the Automatic Pipet:

- The automatic pipet is designed to deliver specific volumes. Each automatic pipet has a specific range of volumes and accuracy. Never set volumes outside of the pipet's specific range, or use excessive force to turn the push button outside of the pipet's range.

- To set the delivery volume, use the push button on top of the pipet. Turning the pushbutton counterclockwise will increase the delivery volume, and turning the pushbutton clockwise will decrease the delivery volume. Make sure that the desired delivery volume "clicks" into place.

- To eject the tip, press the tip injector with your thumb to release the tip into a suitable waste container. Change tips appropriately to avoid contamination.

- Never lay the pipet on its side, always place on a pipet stand when not in use.

- Before you begin pipetting, check that the tip is firmly attached, and clear of foreign particles.

- Work carefully, always push and release the push button slowly. There are two stops for the push button.

- Hold the pipet straight up and down when aspirating liquids.

- Before transferring solution, rinse the tip 2–3 times with the solution you will be transferring, discard this solution into a waste container.

To pipet:

- Depress the push button to the first stop

- Dip the tip of the pipet tip under the surface of the liquid to a depth of about 1cm. Hold the pipet vertically.

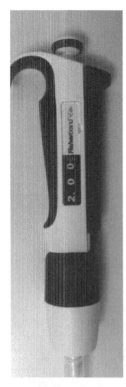

Figure III.7
Automatic Pipet

- Slowly release the push button. Never let the push button snap up. Wait a few seconds to ensure that the full volume of sample is drawn into the plastic tip.
- Withdraw the tip from the liquid, touch the end of the tip against the edge of the container to remove any excess liquid.
- To deliver the liquid to the new container, hold the pipet vertically and depress the push button to the first stop. After a one second delay, depress the push button further to the second stop to empty the tip.
- Slowly release the push button to the ready position. Do not allow the push button to snap back.

Burets

Burets (see Figure III.8) are used in titration experiments where measured delivery of reagents must be made carefully and continuously to .01 of a milliliter.

Do not use soap to clean your buret. Before use, rinse several times with tap water, once deionized water, and once with about 5 mL of titrant. Wet the inside of the buret several times with the 5 mL of titrant.

To properly wet the inside surfaces, tip the buret on its side while holding it in your hand. Be careful not to spill the solution, but make certain the solution comes in contact with the entire length of the buret. Rotate the buret in your hand to wet all inner surfaces. Drain the buret through the stopcock into the waste beaker. Inspect the stopcock to make certain there are no leaks. Leaks can usually be fixed by tightening the stopcock nut. If this does not work, speak to your instructor or get another buret.

Figure III.8
Buret

Always use a funnel to assist in filling the buret.

When filling your buret, lower it to eye level. It may be necessary to remove the buret from the stand in order to do bring it to eye level. NEVER fill the buret above eye level.

Once the buret contains liquid, a beaker (150 mL or larger) should be kept beneath the stop cock at all times in case of leakage.

For proper use, a buret should be perfectly vertical and held so with a buret clamp shown in Appendix II. Most burets have a 50 mL capacity. Fill your buret to the upper graduation by filling to above the graduation and draining carefully until the buret reads 0.00 mL. The graduation are placed 0.10 mL apart but we estimate to one decimal further. Your buret readings will be to 0.01 mL.

Volumetric Flasks

Volumetric flasks (see Figure III.9) are used to make solutions of precise concentrations. These flasks are available in many sizes but the most useful are 25 mL, 50 mL, 100 mL, 500 mL and 1000 mL. These are considered calibrated to 0.01 mL, and so a 100 mL flask will hold exactly 100.00 mL when filled to the graduation line.

Do not use soap to clean your volumetric flask. Before use, rinse several times with tap water, once deionized water, and once with about 5 mL of your solvent (often deionized water). Using a properly sized volumetric pipet or buret, deliver a measured amount of the standardized reagent solution to the volumetric flask.

Fill the flask to the neck with your solvent. Mix the solution by inverting the flask several times. Cover the mouth of the flask with Parafilm to prevent leakage of solution.

Now fill the flask with your solvent until the bottom of the meniscus is at the graduated line. It's helpful to use the polyethylene disposable pipet to add the last few drops of solvent. Again, mix the solution by inverting the flask several times. Cover the mouth of the flask with Parafilm to prevent leakage of solution.

Figure III.9
Volumetric flask

Table IV.1 The Elements

Element	Symbol	Atomic Number	Atomic Mass*	Element	Symbol	Atomic Number	Atomic Mass*
Actinium	Ac	89	(227)	Molybdenum	Mo	42	95.94
Aluminum	Al	13	26.98	Neodymium	Nd	60	144.2
Americium	Am	95	(243)	Neon	Ne	10	20.18
Antimony	Sb	51	121.8	Neptunium	Np	93	(244)
Argon	Ar	18	39.95	Nickel	Ni	28	58.70
Arsenic	As	33	74.92	Niobium	Nb	41	92.91
Astatine	At	85	(210)	Nitrogen	N	7	14.01
Barium	Ba	56	137.3	Nobelium	No	102	(253)
Berkelium	Bk	97	(247)	Osmium	Os	76	190.2
Beryllium	Be	4	9.012	Oxygen	O	8	16.00
Bismuth	Bi	83	209.0	Palladium	Pd	46	106.4
Bohrium	Bh	107	(262)	Phosphorus	P	15	30.97
Boron	B	5	10.81	Platinum	Pt	78	195.1
Bromine	Br	35	79.90	Plutonium	Pu	94	(242)
Cadmium	Cd	48	112.4	Polonium	Po	84	(209)
Calcium	Ca	20	40.08	Potassium	K	19	39.10
Californium	Cf	98	(249)	Praseodymium	Pr	59	140.9
Carbon	C	6	12.01	Promethium	Pm	61	(145)
Cerium	Ce	58	140.1	Protactinium	Pa	91	(231)
Cesium	Cs	55	132.9	Radium	Ra	88	(226)
Chlorine	Cl	17	35.45	Radon	Rn	86	(222)
Chromium	Cr	24	52.00	Rhenium	Re	75	186.2
Cobalt	Co	27	58.93	Rhodium	Rh	45	102.9
Copper	Cu	29	63.55	Rubidium	Rb	37	85.47
Curium	Cm	96	(247)	Ruthenium	Ru	44	101.1
Dubnium	Db	105	(262)	Rutherfordium	Rf	104	(261)
Dysprosium	Dy	66	162.5	Samarium	Sm	62	150.4
Einsteinium	Es	99	(254)	Scandium	Sc	21	44.96
Erbium	Er	68	167.3	Seaborgium	Sg	106	(266)
Europium	Eu	63	152.0	Selenium	Se	34	78.96
Fermium	Fm	100	(253)	Silicon	Si	14	28.09
Fluorine	F	9	19.00	Silver	Ag	47	107.9
Francium	Fr	87	(223)	Sodium	Na	11	22.99
Gadolinium	Gd	64	157.3	Strontium	Sr	38	87.62
Gallium	Ga	31	69.72	Sulfur	S	16	32.07
Germanium	Ge	32	72.61	Tantalum	Ta	73	180.9
Gold	Au	79	197.0	Technetium	Tc	43	(98)
Hafnium	Hf	72	178.5	Tellurium	Te	52	127.6
Hassium	Hs	108	(265)	Terbium	Tb	65	158.9
Helium	He	2	4.003	Thallium	Tl	81	204.4
Holmium	Ho	67	164.9	Thorium	Th	90	232.0
Hydrogen	H	1	1.008	Thulium	Tm	69	168.9
Indium	In	49	114.8	Tin	Sn	50	118.7
Iodine	I	53	126.9	Titanium	Ti	22	47.88
Iridium	Ir	77	192.2	Tungsten	W	74	183.9
Iron	Fe	26	55.85	Uranium	U	92	238.0
Krypton	Kr	36	83.80	Vanadium	V	23	50.94
Lanthanum	La	57	138.9	Xenon	Xe	54	131.3
Lawrencium	Lr	103	(257)	Ytterbium	Yb	70	173.0
Lead	Pb	82	207.2	Yttrium	Y	39	88.91
Lithium	Li	3	6.941	Zinc	Zn	30	65.39
Lutetium	Lu	71	175.0	Zirconium	Zr	40	91.22
Magnesium	Mg	12	24.31			110**	(269)
Manganese	Mn	25	54.94			111	(272)
Meitnerium	Mt	109	(266)			112	(277)
Mendelevium	Md	101	(256)			114	(285)
Mercury	Hg	80	200.6			116	(292)

*All atomic masses are given to four significant figures. Values in parentheses represent the mass number of the most stable isotope.
**The names and symbols for elements 110–112, 114, and 116 have not been chosen.

Table IV.2 Standard Thermodynamic Values
for Selected Substances at 298 K

Substance or ion	ΔH_f^0 (kJ/mol)	ΔG_f^0 (kJ/mol)	S^0 (J/mol·K)
$e^-(g)$	0	0	20.87
Aluminum			
$Al(s)$	0	0	28.3
$Al^{3+}(aq)$	−524.7	−481.2	−313
$AlCl_3(s)$	−704.2	−628.9	110.7
$Al_2O_3(s)$	−1676	−1582	50.94
Barium			
$Ba(s)$	0	0	62.5
$Ba(g)$	175.6	144.8	170.28
$Ba^{2+}(g)$	1649.9	—	—
$Ba^{2+}(aq)$	−538.36	−560.7	13
$BaCl_2(s)$	−806.06	−810.9	126
$BaCO_3(s)$	−1219	−1139	112
$BaO(s)$	−548.1	−520.4	72.07
$BaSO_4(s)$	−1465	−1353	132
Boron			
$B(\beta-\text{rhombohedral})$	0	0	5.87
$BF_3(g)$	−1137.0	−1120.3	254.0
$BCl_3(g)$	−403.8	−388.7	290.0
$B_2H_6(g)$	35	86.6	232.0
$B_2O_3(s)$	−1272	−1193	53.8
$H_3BO_3(s)$	−1094.3	−969.01	88.83
Bromine			
$Br_2(l)$	0	0	152.23
$Br_2(g)$	30.91	3.13	245.38
$Br(g)$	111.9	82.40	174.90
$Br^-(g)$	−218.9	—	—
$Br^-(aq)$	−120.9	−102.82	80.71
$HBr(g)$	−36.3	−53.5	198.59
Cadmium			
$Cd(s)$	0	0	51.5
$Cd(g)$	112.8	78.20	167.64
$Cd^{2+}(aq)$	−72.38	−77.74	−61.1
$CdS(s)$	−144	−141	71
Calcium			
$Ca(s)$	0	0	41.6
$Ca(g)$	192.6	158.9	154.78
$Ca^{2+}(g)$	1934.1	—	—
$Ca^{2+}(aq)$	−542.96	−553.04	−55.2
$CaF_2(s)$	−1215	−1162	68.87
$CaCl_2(s)$	−795.0	−750.2	114
$CaCO_3(s)$	−1206.9	−1128.8	92.9
$CaO(s)$	−635.1	−603.5	38.2
$Ca(OH)_2(s)$	−986.09	−898.56	83.39
$Ca_3(PO_4)_2(s)$	−4138	−3899	263
$CaSO_4(s)$	−1432.7	−1320.3	107
Carbon			
$C(\text{graphite})$	0	0	5.686
$C(\text{diamond})$	1.896	2.866	2.439
$C(g)$	715.0	669.6	158.0
$CO(g)$	−110.5	−137.2	197.5
$CO_2(g)$	−393.5	−394.4	213.7
$CO_2(aq)$	−412.9	−386.2	121
$CO_3^{2-}(aq)$	−676.26	−528.10	−53.1
$HCO_3^-(aq)$	−691.11	587.06	95.0
$H_2CO_3(aq)$	−698.7	−623.42	191
$CH_4(g)$	−74.87	−50.81	186.1
$C_2H_2(g)$	227	209	200.85
$C_2H_4(g)$	52.47	68.36	219.22
$C_2H_6(g)$	−84.667	−32.89	229.5
$C_3H_8(g)$	−105	−24.5	269.9
$C_4H_{10}(g)$	−126	−16.7	310
$C_6H_6(l)$	49.0	124.5	172.8
$CH_3OH(g)$	−201.2	−161.9	238
$CH_3OH(l)$	−238.6	−166.2	127
$HCHO(g)$	−116	−110	219
$HCOO^-(aq)$	−410	−335	91.6
$HCOOH(l)$	−409	−346	129.0
$HCOOH(aq)$	−410	−356	164
$C_2H_5OH(l)$	−277.63	−174.8	161
$C_2H_5OH(g)$	−235.1	−168.6	282.6
$CH_3CHO(g)$	−166	−133.7	266
$CH_3COOH(l)$	−487.0	−392	160
$C_6H_{12}O_6(s)$	−1273.3	−910.56	212.1
$CN^-(aq)$	151	166	118
$HCN(g)$	135	125	201.7
$HCN(l)$	105	121	112.8
$HCN(aq)$	105	112	129
$CS_2(g)$	117	66.9	237.79
$CS_2(l)$	87.9	63.6	151.0
$CH_3Cl(g)$	−83.7	−60.2	234
$CH_2Cl_2(l)$	−117	−63.2	179
$CHCl_3(l)$	−132	−71.5	203
$CCl_4(g)$	−96.0	−53.7	309.7
$CCl_4(l)$	−139	−68.6	214.4
$COCl_2(g)$	−220	−206	283.74
Cesium			
$Cs(s)$	0	0	85.15
$Cs(g)$	76.7	49.7	175.5
$Cs^+(g)$	458.5	427.1	169.72
$Cs^+(aq)$	−248	−282.0	133
$CsF(s)$	−554.7	−525.4	88
$CsCl(s)$	−442.8	−414	101.18
$CsBr(s)$	−395	−383	121
$CsI(s)$	−337	−333	130
Chlorine			
$Cl_2(g)$	0	0	223.0
$Cl(g)$	121.0	105.0	165.1

Substance or ion	ΔH_f^0 (kJ/mol)	ΔG_f^0 (kJ/mol)	S^0 (J/mol·K)	Substance or ion	ΔH_f^0 (kJ/mol)	ΔG_f^0 (kJ/mol)	S^0 (J/mol·K)
$Cl^-(g)$	−234	−240	153.25	**Lithium**			
$Cl^-(aq)$	−167.46	−131.17	55.10	$Li(s)$	0	0	29.10
$HCl(g)$	−92.31	−95.30	186.79	$Li(g)$	161	128	138.67
$HCl(aq)$	−167.46	−131.17	55.06	$Li^+(g)$	687.163	649.989	132.91
$ClO_2(g)$	102	120	256.7	$Li^+(aq)$	−278.46	−293.8	14
$Cl_2O(g)$	80.3	97.9	266.1	$LiF(s)$	−616.9	−588.7	35.66
Chromium				$LiCl(s)$	−408	−384	59.30
$Cr(s)$	0	0	23.8	$LiBr(s)$	−351	−342	74.1
$Cr^{3+}(aq)$	−1971	—	—	$LiI(s)$	−270	−270	85.8
$CrO_4^{2-}(aq)$	−863.2	−706.3	38	**Magnesium**			
$Cr_2O_7^{2-}(aq)$	−1461	−1257	214	$Mg(s)$	0	0	32.69
Copper				$Mg(g)$	150	115	148.55
$Cu(s)$	0	0	33.1	$Mg^{2+}(g)$	2351	—	—
$Cu(g)$	341.1	301.4	166.29	$Mg^{2+}(aq)$	−461.96	−456.01	118
$Cu^+(aq)$	51.9	50.2	−26	$MgCl_2(s)$	−641.6	−592.1	89.630
$Cu^{2+}(aq)$	64.39	64.98	−98.7	$MgCO_3(s)$	−1112	−1028	65.86
$Cu_2O(s)$	−168.6	−146.0	93.1	$MgO(s)$	−601.2	−569.0	26.9
$CuO(s)$	−157.3	−130	42.63	$Mg_3N_2(s)$	−461	−401	88
$Cu_2S(s)$	−79.5	−86.2	120.9	**Manganese**			
$CuS(s)$	−53.1	−53.6	66.5	$Mn(s, \alpha)$	0	0	31.8
Fluorine				$Mn^{2+}(aq)$	−219	−223	−84
$F_2(g)$	0	0	202.7	$MnO_2(s)$	−520.9	−466.1	53.1
$F(g)$	78.9	61.8	158.64	$MnO_4^-(aq)$	−518.4	−425.1	190
$F^-(g)$	−255.6	−262.5	145.47	**Mercury**			
$F^-(aq)$	−329.1	−276.5	−9.6	$Hg(l)$	0	0	76.027
$HF(g)$	−273	−275	173.67	$Hg(g)$	61.30	31.8	174.87
Hydrogen				$Hg^{2+}(aq)$	171	164.4	−32
$H_2(g)$	0	0	130.6	$Hg_2^{2+}(aq)$	172	153.6	84.5
$H(g)$	218.0	203.30	114.60	$HgCl_2(s)$	−230	−184	144
$H^+(aq)$	0	0	0	$Hg_2Cl_2(s)$	−264.9	−210.66	196
$H^+(g)$	1536.3	1517.1	108.83	$HgO(s)$	−90.79	−58.50	70.27
Iodine				**Nitrogen**			
$I_2(s)$	0	0	116.14	$N_2(g)$	0	0	191.5
$I_2(g)$	62.442	19.38	260.58	$N(g)$	473	456	153.2
$I(g)$	106.8	70.21	180.67	$N_2O(g)$	82.05	104.2	219.7
$I^-(g)$	−194.7	—	—	$NO(g)$	90.29	86.60	210.65
$I^-(aq)$	−55.94	−51.67	109.4	$NO_2(g)$	33.2	51	239.9
$HI(g)$	25.9	1.3	206.33	$N_2O_4(g)$	9.16	97.7	304.3
Iron				$N_2O_5(g)$	11	118	346
$Fe(s)$	0	0	27.3	$N_2O_5(s)$	−43.1	114	178
$Fe^{3+}(aq)$	−47.7	−10.5	−293	$NH_3(g)$	−45.9	−16	193
$Fe^{2+}(aq)$	−87.9	−84.94	113	$NH_3(aq)$	−80.83	26.7	110
$FeCl_2(s)$	−341.8	−302.3	117.9	$N_2H_4(l)$	50.63	149.2	121.2
$FeCl_3(s)$	−399.5	−334.1	142	$NO_3^-(aq)$	−206.57	−110.5	146
$FeO(s)$	−272.0	−251.4	60.75	$HNO_3(l)$	−173.23	−79.914	155.6
$Fe_2O_3(s)$	−825.5	−743.6	87.400	$HNO_3(aq)$	−206.57	−110.5	146
$Fe_3O_4(s)$	−1121	−1018	145.3	$NF_3(g)$	−125	−83.3	260.6
Lead				$NOCl(g)$	51.71	66.07	261.6
$Pb(s)$	0	0	64.785	$NH_4Cl(s)$	−314.4	−203.0	94.6
$Pb^{2+}(aq)$	1.6	−24.3	21	**Oxygen**			
$PbCl_2(s)$	−359	−314	136	$O_2(g)$	0	0	205.0
$PbO(s)$	−218	−198	68.70	$O(g)$	249.2	231.7	160.95
$PbO_2(s)$	−276.6	−219.0	76.6	$O_3(g)$	143	163	238.82
$PbS(s)$	−98.3	−96.7	91.3	$OH^-(aq)$	−229.94	−157.30	−10.54
$PbSO_4(s)$	−918.39	−811.24	147	$H_2O(g)$	−241.826	−228.60	188.72

Substance or ion	ΔH_f^0 (kJ/mol)	ΔG_f^0 (kJ/mol)	S^0 (J/mol·K)
$H_2O(l)$	−285.840	−237.192	69.940
$H_2O_2(l)$	−187.8	−120.4	110
$H_2O_2(aq)$	−191.2	−134.1	144
Phosphorus			
$P_4(s,\ white)$	0	0	41.1
$P(g)$	314.6	278.3	163.1
$P(s,\ red)$	−17.6	−12.1	22.8
$P_2(g)$	144	104	218
$P_4(g)$	58.9	24.5	280
$PCl_3(g)$	−287	−268	312
$PCl_3(l)$	−320	−272	217
$PCl_5(g)$	−402	−323	353
$PCl_5(s)$	−443.5	—	—
$P_4O_{10}(s)$	−2984	−2698	229
$PO_4^{3-}(aq)$	−1266	−1013	−218
$HPO_4^{2-}(aq)$	−1281	−1082	−36
$H_2PO_4^-(aq)$	−1285	−1135	89.1
$H_3PO_4(aq)$	−1277	−1019	228
Potassium			
$K(s)$	0	0	64.672
$K(g)$	89.2	60.7	160.23
$K^+(g)$	514.197	481.202	154.47
$K^+(aq)$	−251.2	−282.28	103
$KF(s)$	−568.6	−538.9	66.55
$KCl(s)$	−436.7	−409.2	82.59
$KBr(s)$	−394	−380	95.94
$KI(s)$	−328	−323	106.39
$KOH(s)$	−424.8	−379.1	78.87
$KClO_3(s)$	−397.7	−296.3	143.1
$KClO_4(s)$	−432.75	−303.2	151.0
Rubidium			
$Rb(s)$	0	0	69.5
$Rb(g)$	85.81	55.86	169.99
$Rb^+(g)$	495.04	—	—
$Rb^+(aq)$	−246	−282.2	124
$RbF(s)$	−549.28	—	—
$RbCl(s)$	−435.35	−407.8	95.90
$RbBr(s)$	−389.2	−378.1	108.3
$RbI(s)$	−328	−326	118.0
Silicon			
$Si(s)$	0	0	18.0
$SiF_4(g)$	−1614.9	−1572.7	282.4
$SiO_2(s)$	−910.9	−856.5	41.5
Silver			
$Ag(s)$	0	0	42.702
$Ag(g)$	289.2	250.4	172.892
$Ag^+(aq)$	105.9	77.111	73.93
$AgF(s)$	−203	−185	84
$AgCl(s)$	−127.03	−109.72	96.11
$AgBr(s)$	−99.51	−95.939	107.1
$AgI(s)$	−62.38	−66.32	114

Substance or ion	ΔH_f^0 (kJ/mol)	ΔG_f^0 (kJ/mol)	S^0 (J/mol·K)
$AgNO_3(s)$	−45.06	19.1	128.2
$Ag_2S(s)$	−31.8	−40.3	146
Sodium			
$Na(s)$	0	0	51.446
$Na(g)$	107.76	77.299	153.61
$Na^+(g)$	609.839	574.877	147.85
$Na^+(aq)$	−239.66	−261.87	60.2
$NaF(s)$	−575.4	−545.1	51.21
$NaCl(s)$	−411.1	−384.0	72.12
$NaBr(s)$	−361	−349	86.82
$NaOH(s)$	−425.609	−379.53	64.454
$Na_2CO_3(s)$	−1130.8	−1048.1	139
$NaHCO_3(s)$	−947.7	−851.9	102
$NaI(s)$	−288	−285	98.5
Strontium			
$Sr(s)$	0	0	54.4
$Sr(g)$	164	110	164.54
$Sr^{2+}(g)$	1784	—	—
$Sr^{2+}(aq)$	−545.51	−557.3	−39
$SrCl_2(s)$	−828.4	−781.2	117
$SrCO_3(s)$	−1218	−1138	97.1
$SrO(s)$	−592.0	−562.4	55.5
$SrSO_4(s)$	−1445	−1334	122
Sulfur			
$S_8(rhombic)$	0	0	31.9
$S_8(monoclinic)$	0.3	0.096	32.6
$S(g)$	279	239	168
$S_2(g)$	129	80.1	228.1
$S_8(g)$	101	49.1	430.211
$S^{2-}(aq)$	41.8	83.7	22
$HS^-(aq)$	−17.7	12.6	61.1
$H_2S(g)$	−20.2	−33	205.6
$H_2S(aq)$	−39	−27.4	122
$SO_2(g)$	−296.8	−300.2	248.1
$SO_3(g)$	−396	−371	256.66
$SO_4^{2-}(aq)$	−907.51	−741.99	17
$HSO_4^-(aq)$	−885.75	−752.87	126.9
$H_2SO_4(l)$	−813.989	−690.059	156.90
$H_2SO_4(aq)$	−907.51	−741.99	17
Tin			
$Sn(white)$	0	0	51.5
$Sn(gray)$	3	4.6	44.8
$SnCl_4(l)$	−545.2	−474.0	259
$SnO_2(s)$	−580.7	−519.7	52.3
Zinc			
$Zn(s)$	0	0	41.6
$Zn(g)$	130.5	94.93	160.9
$Zn^{2+}(aq)$	−152.4	−147.21	−106.5
$ZnO(s)$	−348.0	−318.2	43.9
$ZnS(s,\ zinc\ blende)$	−203	−198	57.7

Table IV.3 Selected Water Vapor Pressures

Temp, °C	Vapor pressure, (torr)	Temp, °C	Vapor pressure, (torr)
15	12.8	22	19.8
16	13.6	23	21.1
17	14.5	24	22.4
18	15.5	25	23.8
19	16.5	26	25.2
20	17.5	27	26.8
21	18.7	28	28.4

Table IV.4 Density of Pure Water

Temp, °C	Density g/cm³
0 (solid)	0.9150
0 (liquid)	0.9999
4	1.0000
10	0.9997
15	0.9991
20	0.9982
25	0.9970
30	0.9956
40	0.9922
60	0.9832
80	0.9718

Glossary

Absolute temperature: Temperature measured in Kelvins. Equal to °C + 273.15.

Absorbance: A unitless, quantitative measure of the process of light absorption. It is calculated from the percent transmittance (%T), and can be used with Beer's Law to calculate the concentration of solutions that absorb light.

Absorbance spectrum: The absorbance vs. wavelength relationship for a particular species.

Accuracy: How close a measurement is to the actual value.

Analytical balance: balance that has a total capacity of 100–200 g with a precision of 0.0001g and a glass enclosure to minimize the effects of air movement. Has greater precision than a top loading balance, but a lower capacity.

Anion: Negatively charged ion, often a nonmetal. The negative charge is often attained when accepting one or more electrons in the formation of an ionic compound.

Antioxidant: A molecule capable of inhibiting the oxidation of other molecules by being oxidized themselves and acting as a reducing agent.

Arrhenius Acid: Substance that produces H^+ ions when dissolved in water.

Arrhenius Base: Substance that produces OH^- ions when dissolved in water.

Avogadro's Law: If the pressure, volume and temperature between two gas samples are the same, then the two samples must contain the same number of gas particles.

Back-titration: An analytical technique where the remaining reagents after a reaction are studied in lieu of directly studying the reaction itself.

Balanced chemical equation: An equation representing a chemical reaction in which the number of atoms of each species are the same on both sides of the equation.

Beer's Law (Beer-Lambert's Law): A stated relationship that the Absorbance of a solution is equal to the product of the concentration of a solution, the distance light must travel, and the molar absorptivity of the species.

Boyle's Law: The pressure of a gas held at constant temperature is inversely proportional to its volume, $P \propto 1/V$.

Bunsen Burner: Laboratory equipment that produces a single gas flame.

Buret: Volumetric glassware used for continuous measured delivery of reagent, often in titrations.

Calibration: Method for standardizing an instrument by comparing a measurement to a known standard.

Calorimeter: An insulated container used to measure the heat released or absorbed by the contents.

Calorimeter Constant: A measurement of the amount of heat absorbed by a calorimeter, usually given in units J/°C or J/K.

Capillary action: Causes liquid to rise through a narrow space against gravity.

Catalyst: A substance that increases the rate of a reaction without being consumed in the reaction.

Cation: Positively charged ion, often a metal. The positive charge is often attained when losing one or more electrons in the formation of an ionic compound.

Charles's Law: For a fixed sample of at a fixed pressure, the volume of the gas is proportional to its temperature.

Chemical property: A characteristic of a substance that appears only during a chemical reaction or chemical change of that substance. Ex: enthalpy of formation, heat of combustion, flammability.

Chemical separation: A separation of components that involves a chemical change.

Chromatography: An analytical separation technique that takes advantage of the differences in attraction of components to either a mobile or stationary phase.

Colorimeter: A device used for measuring the light that passes through a sample.

Combined Gas Law: An expression that relates the volume, temperature, and pressure of a gas.

Complete ionic equation: A written chemical reaction in which all soluble species are present in their dissociated form as ions in solution. Insoluble species are not shown as dissociated.

Compound: A substance composed of two or more elements in fixed proportions. Each compound has a unique set of chemical and physical properties that can be used to identify, differentiate, and classify the substance.

Coordination complex: An ion consisting of a central atom (usually a metal cation) that becomes bonded covalently to polar molecules and/or anions (called ligands) when the ligand donates a pair of electrons to the central atom (a coordinate covalent bond).

Coordinate covalent bond: A chemical bond involving shared electrons; a coordinate covalent bond is formed when one species donates a pair of electrons to the covalent bond.

Covalent compounds: Compounds in which electrons are shared and are usually identified by comparing their physical properties (such as boiling point or refractive index).

Crystallization (separation technique): Separation and purification of components of a mixture by taking advantage of the differing freezing points or differing solubilites of the components.

Dalton's Law of Partial Pressures: In a mixture of unreacting gases, the total pressure of the mixture is equal to the sum of the partial pressures of each of the constituent gases.

DCP (2,6-dichloroindophenol): An oxidizing agent used in the redox titration of vitamin C.

Decantation: "Pouring off" method for separating a liquid from the solid. The liquid portion (supernatant) is poured off and discarded, leaving the solid component behind.

Density: An instensive physical property of all substances. Denisty is the mass per unit volume, symbolized by rho, ρ. Density, $\rho = mass/volume$, often expressed as g/cm^3, g/ L, kg/m^3, or lb/ft^3.

Dissolving: Dissolution is the process of creating a solution from a solid and a liquid.

Distillation: A separation and purification technique that separates components of a mixture by taking advantage of the different boiling points of the components.

Electronegativity: The tendency of an atom to attract electrons in a covalent bond.

Element: A substance that is not composed of other substances that has a unique set of chemical and physical properties. An element is composed of only one type of atom.

Endothermic process: A process that absorbs heat from the surroundings and therefore increases the enthalpy of the system. An endothermic process has a positive change in enthalpy.

Enthalpy: Heat exchanged at constant pressure.

Entropy: Thermodynamic measure of disorder.

Equivalence point: The point in a titration where the number of moles of acid equals in solution the number of moles of base in solution.

Exothermic process: A process that releases heat to the surrounding and therefore decreases the enthalpy of the system. An exothermic process has a negative change in enthalpy.

Extensive property: A characteristic that depends on the quantity of a substance. Ex: mass or volume.

Filtrate: The soluble component of a filtered mixture.

Filtration: Method for separating a liquid from a solid that involves passing the liquid through a medium that removes the solid component.

First Law of Thermodynamics: The total energy in any process is conserved.

Flame test: A method of characterizing a substance based on the color a flame turns when that substance is burned. Compounds or elements often can be distinguished by a characteristic color of flame.

Fractional crystallization: A separation technique that takes advantage of differences in solubility between components in a mixture at a given temperature.

Gas-Liquid Chromatography: A separation technique useful for separating mixtures of gases or components that can be vaporized without thermally decomposing.

Gay-Lussac's Law: For a fixed sample of gas at constant volume, the pressure of the gas is directly proportional to its temperature.

Graduated cylinder: A type of volumetric glassware used to measure approximate volumes of a liquid. In general, smaller graduated cylinders are more precise than larger ones.

Heat: The energy transferred between objects because of differing temperatures.

Heat capacity: The amount of heat required to change the temperature of an object by 1 degree Celsius (or 1 K).

High-Performance Liquid Chromatography (HPLC): Chromatography method useful for separating components that would decompose if they were vaporized, such as carbohydrates and biological molecules.

Heterogeneous mixture: A mixture that is not uniform on the molecular level and often has visual boundaries between its components.

Homogeneous mixture: A mixture that is uniform all the way down to the molecular level, a solution.

Hydrate: Compounds that have a specific number of water molecules associated.

Ideal Gas Law: A relationship between the pressure, volume, number of molecules, and speed of ideal gas particles. $PV = nRT$.

Insoluble: Compounds that have extremely low tendency to dissolve in a given solvent.

Instensive property: A characteristic of a substance that is independent of the quantity of that substance. Ex: density, index of refraction.

Intermolecular forces: Electrostatic forces between molecules- in general intermolecular forces are relatively strong between liquids and solids and much weaker for gases.

Ionic compound: Compounds in which electrons are transferred, leaving oppositely charged ions.

Lewis acid: A species that accepts an electron pair.

Lewis structures: A structural formula consisting of electron dot symbols and lines to represent chemical bonds.

Ligand: A molecule or anion covalently bonded to a central metal ion in a complex.

Limiting reagent: A reagent that is consumed completely in a chemical reaction. The limiting reagent therefore determines the extent of the reaction and the amount of product that forms.

Mean: The average of a series of measurements.

Meniscus: The concave (or convex) surface of a solution or pure liquid in a glass container (often graduated cylinder). The meniscus forms as a result of cohesive forces between the liquid molecules and adhesive forces between the liquid and the glass.

Mixture: Two or more elements and/or compounds which are physically intermingled.

Mobile phase: Chromatography constituent that carries the components of a mixture.

Mohr pipet: Graduated pipet used to measure and deliver a range of volumes.

Molar absorptivity: A species-specific measurement of how strongly light is absorbed by that species at a given wavelength.

Molar heat capacity: The amount of heat required to change the temperature of one mole of a substance by 1 degree Celsius (or 1 K).

Molecular chemical equation: A written chemical reaction in which all aqueous ionic species are represented in their undissociated forms in solution.

Net ionic equation: A written chemical reaction in where all liquid, solid and gaseous species are represented, but all spectator ions have been removed- leaving only the aqueous ions directly involved in the reaction.

Octet rule: The general rule that when atoms bond, they tend to lose or gain electrons in order to attain an outer shell of eight electrons.

Oxidation: The loss of electrons.

Oxidizing agent: A species that causes another to be oxidized and is in turn reduced—a chemical species that gains electrons in an oxidation-reduction reaction.

Oxoanion: A multi-atom negatively charged ion consisting of one or more elements bonded to oxygen.

Paper Chromatography: A separation technique that uses paper as the stationary phase.

Parallax: The apparent displacement of an object as seen from different points that are on different lines of sight to the object.

Path length: The distance light must travel through a sample in a spectrophotometry/colorimetry experiment. Often set to 1cm for convenience.

Peak absorbance wavelength: The wavelength at which maximum absorbance of light occurs for a particular chemical species. When this wavelength is in the visible light region it corresponds to a particular color of light absorbed.

pH: the negative log of the concentration of hydronium ions in an aqueous solution; a measure of acidity.

Physical property: A measurable characteristic of a substance that is shown by the substance itself without a chemical reaction. Ex: color, mass, density.

Physical separation: A separation of components that does not involve a chemical change.

Polarity: An asymmetric distribution of electrostatic charge.

Polyatomic ion: An ion in which two or more atoms are bonded covalently.

Precipitate: An insoluble product.

Precision: A measure of how close or reproducible a series of experimental measurements are to each other.

Qualitative analysis: Method of analysis used to identify and ultimately classify matter, as opposed to measuring the quantity of matter.

Qualitative property: characteristics that can be observed but not measured. Ex: color, smell, physical state.

Quantitative property: characteristic that can be measured numerically. Ex: mass, density, volume.

Random error: Error which always present when taking a measurement. Random error values will be both higher and lower than the actual value, and the magnitude of the error is related to the precision of the instrument being used.

Reagent grade: A chemical species with a high enough purity for use in chemical analysis.

Redox reaction: Short for reduction-oxidation reaction; a chemical reaction in which electrons are transferred from a reducing agent to an oxidizing agent.

Redox titration: An analytical technique that uses a known concentration and volume of oxidizing agent to find an unkown concentration of a known volume of reducing agent (or vice versa).

Reducing agent: A species that causes another to be reduced and is in turn oxidized—a chemical species that loses electrons in an oxidation-reduction reaction.

Reduction: A gain of electrons.

Reference blank: A sample used in calibration of the colorimeter which includes the cuvet, solvent and all additives excluding the species being studied.

Relative experimental error: The difference between the actual value and the experimental result, divided by the actual value.

Resolution: In chromatography, relative separation of the components, quantified by the differences in retention factors.

Retention Factor: Quantitative measure of the separation of components in chromatography: how far the component moves from the origin divided by the distance the solvent front moved.

Saturated solution: A solution that contains the maximum amount of a dissolved solute at a given temperature.

Scientific notation: A system to represent numbers both large and small without ambiguity regarding significant figures.

Siphon: A watertight system that allows liquid to move between two containers with differences in pressure.

Solubility: A measure of the maximum amount of solute that will dissolve in a particular amount of specific solvent at a given temperature. Often given in the units g/L or mol/L.

Soluble: Compounds that dissolve in a given solvent to form aqueous species.

Solute: The minor component(s) of a solution.

Solution: A homogeneous mixture.

Solvent: The major component of the solution in which the solute is dissolved.

Solvent front: The leading edge of the solvent as it moves through the stationary phase.

Specific heat capacity: The amount of heat required to change the temperature of one gram of a substance by 1 degree Celsius (or 1 K).

Spectator ions: Ions that are present as dissociated on both sides of the chemical equation and do not participate directly in the chemical reaction.

Spectophotometry: The study of electromagnetic spectra, often by measuring light absorption.

Standard: A solution or substance of a measured, known concentration.

Standard deviation: How far apart the individual measurements are from the mean.

$$\delta = \sqrt{\frac{1}{n-1}\sum_{1}^{n}(\overline{x}-x_i)^2}$$

Standardization: Process to determine the actual concentration of a reagent.

State function: A property of a system that is determined only by its current state and not how the current state was reached.

Stationary phase: Chromatography component through which the mobile phase moves.

Stock system: Set of rules used to categorize and name inorganic chemical compounds.

Stoichiometry: The study of the molar relationships in a chemical reaction.

Strong acid: An acid that completely ionizes in water.

Strong base: A base that completely ionizes in water.

Structural formula: A chemical formula that shows the placement of atoms in molecules and the bonds between them.

Supersaturated: An unstable solution in which more solute is dissolved than in the saturated solution.

Systematic error: Error which is consistently higher or lower than the actual value. This type of error results from either a faulty measuring device or an operator consistently making an incorrect reading.

Temperature: A measure of the average kinetic energy of a substance. Also a measurement of how hot or cold a substance is relative to another substance.

Thermodynamics: The study of heat flow.

Thin Layer Chromatography: A type of chromatography where a thin layer of silica gel, alumina or cellulose on a glass plate is used as the stationary phase. The solvent used as the mobile phase is drawn through the stationary phase using capillary action.

Top loading balance: A balance that has a large capacity, but with lower precision and no glass enclosure.

Transfer Pipet: Pipet calibrated to deliver only one volume.

Transmittance: A measure of light that passes through a sample.

Universal gas constant: The proportionality constant that relates the pressure, volume, temperature and number of molecules in an ideal gas. $R = PV/nT$

Unsaturated: A solution that contains less than the maximum amount of a dissolved solute at a given temperature.

Visible light spectrum: The portion of the electromagnetic spectrum that is visible to the human eye. Visible light has a wavelength of approximately 380 nm to 740 nm.

Volumetric flask: Type of volumetric glassware used to make solutions of precise concentrations.

Volumetric glassware: Used to make precise volume measurements in the laboratory. Includes pipets, burets, and volumetric flasks.

Weak acid: An acid that does not completely ionize in water.

Weak base: A base that does not completely ionize in water.

Work: The energy transferred when an object is moved by a force over a certain distance.